J Stewart.

FOOTPRINTS OF EARLY MAN

BLACKIE & SON LIMITED
50 Old Bailey, LONDON
17 Stanhope Street, GLASGOW

BLACKIE & SON (INDIA) LIMITED
Warwick House, Fort Street, BOMBAY

BLACKIE & SON (CANADA) LIMITED
1118 Bay Street, TORONTO

IN THE GREAT LIMESTONE QUARRY, NEAR IPSWICH

J. Reid Moir is pointing to the Sub-red Crag Flint Tool layer of Pliocene Age, by far the most ancient evidence of man thus far discovered. Professor Osborn stands under the Red-crag summit, on the level of the Foxhall Tool layer

Photograph by C. Forster Cooper of Cambridge University

FOOTPRINTS OF EARLY MAN

BY

DONALD A. MACKENZIE

Author of "Ancient Man in Britain"
"Wonder Tales from Scottish Myth and Legend" &c.

BLACKIE & SON LIMITED
LONDON AND GLASGOW
1927

Printed in Great Britain by
Blackie & Son, Limited, Glasgow

PREFACE

The vastness of the antiquity of man is revealed by Mr. J. Reid Moir's notable discovery of finely worked flints in and beneath the Red Crag of Suffolk. In our study of early human relics we are therefore taken back to the remote Upper Pliocene Age, " namely ", as Professor Henry Fairfield Osborn puts it, " to a period six million years before our era ". The earliest settlers in East Anglia were thus chipping flint with wonderful skill at a time when there was yet no English Channel, and the waters of the North Sea were as warm as those which wash round the Bahama Islands at the present day. So far, we possess no precise knowledge as to what those early craftsmen and hunters were like. It may be that they bore a resemblance to Piltdown man, whose skull, as reconstructed by Professor G. Elliot Smith, is reproduced in these pages. The geological horizon of this now-famous relic is uncertain, but the view that it is of earlier date than was at first supposed cannot be ignored. Future finds may help to clarify that aspect of an interesting problem.

In this volume Early Man is dealt with in relation to the various geological epochs from the Tertiary period till the " dawn " of the historical period when the climate of Europe had become pretty much what it is to-day. As far back as we can go, man appears before us as an intelligent, thinking being who did things because there were reasons for doing them and "sought out many inventions". Even man of the extinct Neanderthal species can be shown to have been a thinker, not only on the evidence of burial customs, but also on that afforded by the recent discoveries in an Austrian cave (Chapter VI) which prove him to have been resourceful and courageous in the quest for food. In that dark cave Neanderthal man can be said to have demonstrated the superiority of brain power above mere brute strength.

Other recent discoveries which are dealt with in this volume are those of the Galilee, Rhodesian, and "Lady of Lloyds" skulls, and of the bones of Pleistocene animals taken from the asphalt beds of California which reveal so wonderful and exact a story. Summaries are likewise given of the archæological finds made by expeditions which have of late visited China and the Gobi desert, and of the traces of Early Man which have been brought to light on the American Continent. It will be found that certain fresh views and facts regarding the activities in Western Europe of the ancestors of modern men tend to throw further light on problems which are nowadays engaging world-wide attention and interest. The cave art is considered, and the outstanding traces of post-glacial settlements in Britain passed under review, account being taken of the recent identification of pre-Neolithic finds in Scotland.

From the Hunting Period of the archæologists, the narrative passes to the beginnings of modern civilization which is rooted in the agricultural mode of life. A chapter is devoted to the available evidence regarding the discovery of agriculture, and another to the invention of boats and the subsequent development of navigation which so greatly stimulated the activities of the pioneers of civilization. Further chapters deal with the rise and growth of civilization in ancient Egypt, ancient Mesopotamia, and ancient Crete, and it is shown that the latter island-kingdom was the "cradle" of European civilization. If it is constantly borne in mind that the world was very thinly peopled indeed during the archæological "Hunting Period", it will be realized that the diffusion, from a particular centre, of the elements of civilization was an inevitable result of the introduction of the agricultural mode of life. In those areas into which agriculture was introduced the population increased considerably, practising and developing acquired crafts and perpetuating acquired religious customs connected with the new mode of life.

The archæological narrative is carried on from the Age of Stone to the Bronze and Iron Ages, and chapters are devoted to the problems presented by the ancient standing stones, the race question, culture drifting, and the language question.

The volume is primarily intended as a convenient, popular summary of the manifold discoveries of recent years which are throwing so much light on the experiences and activities of human beings in their struggle for existence during the vast period before that of recorded history. To the young student and to the general reader it may prove useful as an introduction to a literature of highly technical character which of late years has become voluminous.

DONALD A. MACKENZIE.

CONTENTS

LIST OF PLATES

BIBLIOGRAPHY

The following is a list of the chief works of reference consulted by the writer:

Hugo Obermaier, *Fossil Man in Spain.*
H. F. Osborn, *Men of the Old Stone Age.*
J. Geikie, *Antiquity of Man in Europe.*
J. Reid Moir, *Pre-palæolithic Man.*
H. Breuil, *Revue Anthropologique*, t. xxxii, Paris.
R. Munro, *Palæolithic Man and Terramara Settlements in Europe.*
W. T. Sollas, *Ancient Hunters and Their Modern Representatives.*
M. Boule, *Fossil Men.*
M. C. Burkitt, *Prehistory.*
Lord Avebury, *Prehistoric Times.*
A. Keith, *The Antiquity of Man.*
Clement Reid, *Submerged Forests.*
G. Elliot Smith, *The Ancient Egyptians.*
J. H. Breasted, *The Origins of Civilization.*
G. G. MacCurdy, *Human Origins.*
J. De Morgan, *Prehistoric Man.*
V. G. Childe, *The Dawn of European Civilization.*
A. Evans, *The Palace of Minos.*
G. Glotz, *The Ægean Civilization.*
The Cambridge Ancient History, Vol. I.
J. Dunn, *The Ancient Irish Epic.*
T. Eric Peet, *Rough Stone Monuments.*
G. Sergi, *The Mediterranean Race.*
W. Z. Ripley, *The Races of Europe.*
A. C. Haddon, *The Wanderings of Races*; and various Transactions and periodicals, including *Natural History* (New York), Vol. XXV and XXVI, *Nature*, Nov. 7, 1925, and *Discovery* (London) 1925–6.

INTRODUCTORY

"The night of time," wrote Sir Thomas Browne, the famous seventeenth-century Norwich physician, "far surpasseth the day." That "night" is the long prehistoric period during which the ancient peoples in different parts of the world lived under primitive conditions. It was everywhere of much greater duration than the "day of time", that is, the period of recorded history.

In Egypt and Mesopotamia the earliest inscriptions, which usher in the "day" for those limited areas, date back for fifty centuries. We may regard this as a long period, but the most ancient traces of human activities are of vastly greater antiquity. Many thousands of years before men invented writing to express their ideas and record their doings, they had made other inventions more vital to their needs. Human relics have been found which take us back through the long and dark prehistoric period beyond even the Ice Age which began more than half a million years ago. Small and scattered groups of human beings were living in the area we now know as Western Europe long before the British Isles had been separated from the Continent by the English Channel, and before the present river valleys of Europe had been formed; men were chipping flint to make tools and weapons of the chase when the climate of our native land was sub-tropical, and they were here when it was as cold as in Greenland at the present time and a fierce struggle had to be waged for existence. The ancient peoples passed through many geographical changes in the world during the hundreds of thousands of years that elapsed before the first historical records were inscribed on rocks and hewn stones and on baked clay tablets.

An idea of the comparative lengths of the prehistoric and the historic periods may be obtained by an illustration afforded by the clock. Beginning at 12 we move the minute hand round the face to 12.55 to indicate the duration of the prehistoric period. The remaining five minutes to 1 o'clock represent the historic period from the time of the earliest records in Egypt and Mesopotamia till the present day.

It is impossible to give exact dates for the various ages during which great geographical and climatic changes took place in the areas now known as Europe, Asia, Africa, and America. After the early hunters had arrived in the country which was to become known as England, the Arctic ice-sheet spread gradually southward over a great part of Europe on four different occasions. There were therefore four Glacial periods which were separated by many thousands of years. Between these cold periods there were warm Inter-glacial periods which lasted very much longer than did the glaciations. Geologists have endeavoured to estimate the duration of each period, making rough calculations as to the time occupied by the advance and retreat of slowly moving glaciers, and the time occupied in the accumulation of water-laid beds of gravel and soil of considerable depth which are found in some places lying above the glacial deposits. These calculations vary greatly, as is shown by the following estimates of several authorities regarding the total period covered by the Glacial and Inter-glacial epochs of the Ice Age.

Charles Lyell, 800,000 years; J. D. Dana, 720,000 years; C. D. Walcott, 400,000 years; W. Upham, 100,000 years; A. Heim, 100,000 years; W. J. Sollas, 400,000 years; A. Penck, 520,000 to 840,000 years; James Geikie, 620,000 years (minimum); H. F. Osborn, 500,000 years.

The following is one of the recent tables which give in years the proportionate lengths of the various climatic stages of the Ice Age:

1st Glacial epoch, 25,000 years.
1st Inter-glacial epoch, 75,000 years.
2nd Glacial epoch, 25,000 years.
2nd Inter-glacial epoch, 200,000 years.
3rd Glacial epoch, 25,000 years.
3rd Inter-glacial epoch, 100,000 years.
Fourth glacial epoch, 25,000 years.
Post-glacial epoch, 25,000.

According to another system the Ice Age ended about 6000 B.C., and fluctuations of climate followed with changes of sea and land levels.

Geologists and archæologists are not agreed as to the periods in which the early flint-chipping hunters lived in the area we now know as Europe. In the following table two systems are given. That marked *A* is the system of A. Penck and J. Geikie (1914) and that marked *B* the system of Hugo Obermaier (1924):

CHRONOLOGICAL TABLE, *A* AND *B*

1st Glacial epoch (Günz). *A* and *B*. No trace of man.
1st Inter-glacial epoch. *A* and *B*. No trace of man.
2nd Glacial epoch (Mindel). *A* and *B*. No trace of man.
2nd Inter-glacial epoch. *A*. Chellean, Acheulian. *B*. Pre-Chellean (eoliths).
3rd Glacial epoch (Riss). *A*. Mousterian. *B*. Early Chellean(?).

3rd Inter-glacial epoch. *A.* Mousterian, Aurignacian. *B.* Late Chellean, Acheulian.

4th Glacial epoch (Würm). *A.* Solutrean. *B.* Mousterian, Early Aurignacian.

Post-glacial epoch. *A.* Magdalenian. *B.* Late Aurignacian, Solutrean, and Magdalenian.

According to both systems, the Archæological Ages—that is, those marked out by classifying the tools of Early Man—are given in the following order:

EARLY OR LOWER PALÆOLITHIC ("Old Stone") AGE. (1) Chellean stage; (2) Acheulian stage; (3) Mousterian stage.

LATE OR UPPER PALÆOLITHIC. (1) Aurignacian; (2) Solutrean; (3) Magdalenian.

These "culture stages" are explained in the chapters that follow, and the tables here given can be referred to as the chapters dealing with the Geological and Archæological Ages are being perused.

Wiegers' Chronological Table

The following is the system of F. Wiegers (1920), in which he shows only three glacial stages:

1st Glacial epoch. Eolithic.
1st Inter-glacial epoch. Chellean, Early Acheulian.
2nd Glacial epoch. Late Acheulian.
2nd Inter-glacial epoch. Early Mousterian.
3rd Glacial epoch. Late Mousterian.
Late 3rd Glacial epoch and Post-glacial epoch } Late Palæolithic (Aurignacian, Solutrean, Magdalenian.

Of late Mr. J. Reid Moir has discovered worked flints called "eoliths" ("dawn stones") in and beneath the Red Crag of Suffolk. It is now generally accepted that the oldest of these human relics are of very much earlier date than the First Glacial epoch. The tables given above were compiled before

Mr. Moir's remarkable finds were fully appreciated and accepted. The following new geological time scale has been prepared by Professor Henry Fairfield Osborn:—

		Minimum Age (Years) Based on Uranium-Lead-Helium Content.	Round Numbers for Reference (Years).
QUATERNARY—(Age of Man)	Recent ... ... / Pleistocene ...	1,000,000	1,000,000
TERTIARY—(Age of Mammals)	Pliocene	6,000,000	50,000,000
	Miocene	12,000,000	
	Oligocene	16,000,000	
	Eocene	20,000,000	
MESOZOIC—(Age of Reptiles)			150,000,000
PALÆOZOIC (Age of Fishes and Amphibians) ...			300,000,000
PRECAMBRIAN			1,000,000,000

Actual discovery of man now reaches into Upper Pliocene time, namely, to a period 6,000,000 years before our era.

Dealing with Egypt, Professor J. H. Breasted places the earliest relics of man in the Nile Valley as far back as the First Glacial epoch of Europe. At that time the area we now know as Egypt was occupied by an inland lake and men lived on the present cliff tops. During the Third Interglacial and the Fourth Glacial epochs of Europe, the Egyptian lake had vanished and the River Nile, having cut out its bed, was depositing soil along its banks. During Europe's Fourth Glacial epoch the prehistoric Egyptians were making pottery, fragments of which have been obtained in borings through the Nile-laid alluvium at depths of from 35 to 80 feet. During Europe's Post-glacial epoch the Egyptians had discovered agriculture and were domesticating animals. According to

Breasted, copper and gold were used in Egypt before 4000 B.C., and Egyptian boats were rowed across the Mediterranean before 3000 B.C.

In Europe the last phase of Palæolithic civilization, which is known as the Magdalenian, was followed at the close of the Post-glacial epoch by what the archæologists call the "Transition period", during which there were three industries named the Azilian, the Tardenoisian, and the Maglemosian. These were followed in turn by the following Archæological Ages:

(1) Neolithic Age.
(2) Eneolithic or Copper Age.
(3) Bronze Age.
(4) Iron Age.

The Neolithic or New Stone Age of Northern Europe is dated by Montelius, the French archæologist, 3500–1700 B.C.; the Bronze Age, 1800–700 B.C.; and the Iron Age, 700–500 B.C. L. Siret, the Belgian archæologist, however, gives the following dates, calculated from the discoveries made in Spain:

End of Neolithic Age, 1500 B.C.
Eneolithic or Copper Age, 1200 B.C.
Bronze Age, 1200–800 B.C.
Iron Age, 800–200 B.C.

Osborn, on the other hand, dates the introduction of copper in Egypt and Mesopotamia as far back as 5000 B.C.; in Troy, Greece, Sicily, Hungary, and Spain, 3000 B.C.; and in Northern and Central Europe and in France, 2500 B.C. He gives the introduction of bronze in Mesopotamia at 3000 B.C.; in Troy, Greece, and Sicily at 2500 B.C.; and Central Europe, France and Spain at 2000 B.C.

It will thus be seen that the authorities are not agreed regarding the dating of the various prehistoric ages.

FOOTPRINTS OF EARLY MAN

CHAPTER I

The Earliest Hunters

Before beginning the story of the earliest hunters we must first glance briefly at the wonderful story of the early world.

The geologists have discovered that the "crust" of the earth is arranged in a series of divisions which they call "beds". These beds belong to different periods of time, and all of them contain traces of ancient life.

The oldest or lowest bed is called the *Primary* system, and it is followed in turn by the *Secondary*, the *Tertiary*, and the *Quaternary* systems.

The *Primary* system contains the remains of early fishes and land plants. In its "later" or "upper" part are the coal measures, which were formed by tree-ferns and other plants.

The *Secondary* system contains the remains of numerous fishes and of the gigantic reptiles, some skeletons of which are preserved in museums. Oak trees, walnut trees, and fig trees have also been traced in this system.

In the *Tertiary* system are the remains of many plants and animals somewhat similar to those of our own time.

The *Quaternary* system has numerous traces of the Great Ice Age, and also of many animals and plants existing at the present day.

All these systems represent vast periods of time—many millions of years—which are usually referred to simply as "ages".

As this book deals with early man our chief interest is in the *Tertiary* (or third) Age, and the *Quaternary* (or fourth) Age, for it is in the beds or layers of these ages that the earliest traces of human beings have been found.

In far-off *Tertiary* times, and many centuries before the beginning of the Great Ice Age, groups of primitive hunters reached and settled in the country which we know as England. They came from the south, but had not to cross the sea, for the area now swept by the surging tides of the English Channel was then a pleasant green valley with silvery rivers and thick rustling woods, while a long unbroken range of grass-covered chalk hills stretched from the North Downs to the land which has been called France.

The North Sea was then as warm as the waters that wash round the West Indies in our own time. There were white and red coral reefs on the coast-line, which then in places curved several miles beyond the present coast-line of eastern England, round to the areas now known as Belgium and Holland. The summers were hot, and the winters brought no frost or snow. One could have cultivated sugar-cane, bananas, and coco-nut trees in England in those far-off times.

Geologists have traced the wonderful history of the Tertiary period in East Anglia, which has been less invaded by the sea than other parts of eastern England. They apply the name "Crag" to various formations or "beds" of gravels and of sands containing ancient shells, &c., which date back to very remote times.

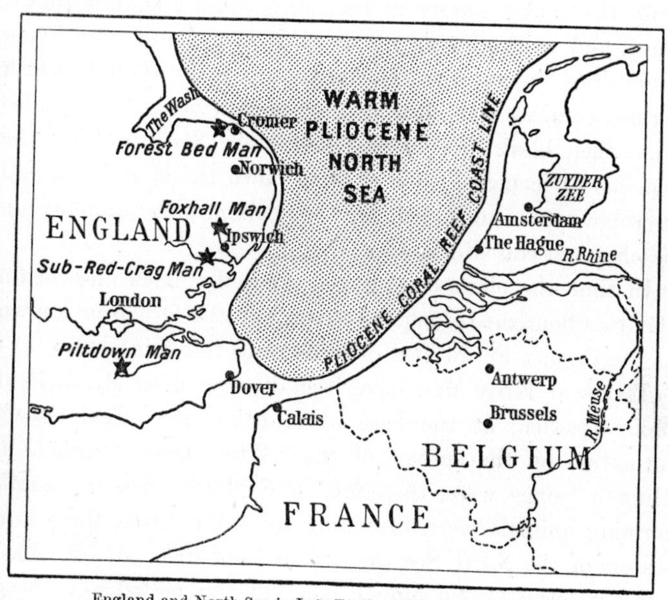

England and North Sea in Late Tertiary Period (after Osborn)

The earliest formation which interests us is the "White Crag" or "Coralline Crag", but it must be borne in mind that "Coralline" does not mean a coral formation. The ancient coral-reef lies above the "White Crag", and as it has been more or less coloured by oxide of iron, it is known as the "Red Crag". Above the "Red Crag" is the later "Norwich Crag", and above the "Norwich Crag" are the "Chillesford beds", and then comes the "Weybourn Crag".

The successive "Crags" tell the story of a gradual cooling of sea and land temperatures. In the older formations the relics of southern or warm-country forms of life are plentiful. Then these decrease in numbers and some vanish. Shell-fish from the colder waters in the north came gradually southward, and in the course of time Arctic molluscs were living round the shores where formerly the little animals which formed coral were at work for thousands of years. The shores were then bleak and treeless and cold. Sheets of ice, the remains of icebergs, came drifting down the North Sea, and in some were embedded big boulders, which stranded on beaches and can still be seen.

In time the climate improved gradually, until once again the trees flourished along the coasts, and the formation known as the Cromer Forest Bed deposits came into existence.

Traces of Early Man have been discovered by Mr. J. Reid Moir, Ipswich, at the base of or below the "Red Crag" formation on the surface of the "White Crag" formation. Human beings were, therefore, in England when the coral-forming animals were beginning to secrete from the warm waters of the North Sea the carbonate of lime, &c., of which coral is formed. No human bones of this period have been brought to light, but numerous flints, which some call "eoliths" (dawn-stones), sharpened and given desired forms by human fingers directed by intelligent minds, testify to man's presence in East Anglia. When the weather was growing cooler men's minds were growing "sharper", and fires were lit to give warmth and to cook food.

When the earliest groups of human hunters reached the Thames Valley in Tertiary times they saw many animals, including reptiles, that do not live in modern England. The

RESTORATION OF A MASTODON

By courtesy of Dr. John M. Clarke, Director of New York State Museum at Albany

hippopotamus cropped the herbage on the site of London and swam and dived in the river. Big tortoises crawled over the gravel and, when the sun was high, dropped into pools to refresh themselves. In the woods were deer with wide antlers, and these were preyed upon by the fierce sabre-tooth tiger which had two long tusks curving downward from its upper jaw. A type of rhinoceros, with sharp horns on its snout, prowled through the bushes, and the powerful mastodon, a variety of elephant, fed on succulent leaves and herbage. Hyænas and wolves were numerous, and there were small and large bears. The giant sloth haunted the forests. It was an uncouth and powerful animal with rougher fur than that of the bear and a shorter and flatter head. On the ground it moved about awkwardly, for its long claws curved inwards, but these enabled it to climb trees and scramble along the branches, hanging downwards.

Among the pretty and harmless animals were little horses with three toes, nimble gazelles and antelopes, and large numbers of land and water birds. In the trees were long-armed apes something like gibbons and also small monkeys.

Traces of the ancient people who lived by hunting are nowadays found chiefly in East Anglia, which, as stated, they certainly reached during the Tertiary period.

We are not sure what Tertiary man looked like, but it is certain he was not particularly tall and powerful. His strength was in his brain. He could think and remember, and he could make his thoughts and experiences known to his fellows by means of speech. The language he spoke had been gradually invented by the generations that had lived before him, and the number of words in use was always increasing.

Wild animals could, as they still do, utter cries that expressed emotions, cries of alarm, anger, pleasure, and so on, but man alone among living creatures was able to tell of what had happened, give instruction to the young, and discuss things that interested him.

Withal, Tertiary man could make plans and lay down rules of conduct and arrange for division of labour so that each member of a community might know and perform his or her duties. It was necessary that the early people should live in groups for their mutual protection.

Early man had one special accomplishment which gave him a great advantage over the big and powerful animals. He used tools which he had made or selected for himself. By working with his hands he helped to develop his brain, and the more his brain developed the more skilful he became. It was as an artisan and a thinker that man became the "lord" of the ancient world.

The earliest tools appear to have been of wood and bone. Before coming to the country now known as England, the hunters had, however, begun to make use of flint. They discovered that this material could be split up and chipped and made into cutting and scraping tools.

Now, flint is harder than iron, but being very brittle it can be more easily worked when a lump (called a nodule) is properly split up. The thin flakes have keen edges that cut like a modern knife. One can sharpen a pencil with a little flake of flint.

At first man may have utilized suitable bits of flint that he had picked up, but, as we find, he soon began to chip selected pieces so that these might be made more useful as tools. Some of the artisans were, no doubt, cleverer than others and invented new forms which in time were generally adopted.

The working of flint demands no little care and skill, as anyone will find who attempts to shape tools like those of the ancient artisans. A nodule of flint which is to be chipped into a handy tool should first be laid on something which yields to a blow and not on a bare stone, otherwise it will be badly shattered.

At first flints were "dressed" by chipping. In time they were divided and the core was used.

The ancient flint-worker probably used a bit of turf which was laid on some harder substance. Placing the selected flint nodule on this "pad", he struck it with a stone and split it. A quick deft blow or two separated flakes of different sizes. Selecting one piece which came nearest to the form he wanted, he used a smaller and pointed piece to chip and scrape it round the edges. When this was being done the larger flint was held tightly in the one hand and the smaller one in the other.

Some flints were used as tools to make tools, some to shape other flint implements, and some to shape tools of wood and bone by means of scraping.

The most ancient flint implements are nowadays discovered in gravel pits, old river terraces, &c., along with the bones of Pliocene animals or other relics of that far-distant age.

It is not always easy to distinguish "eoliths" which have been partly shaped by human hands from flints that have been flaked by pressure in the soil or by being rolled in river gravel. When, however, it is found that collectors have picked up quite a number of specimens that had been chipped in exactly the same way and from the same angles, it becomes apparent that such regular and systematic chipping could not have been purely accidental—the result of mere chance. We have to conclude that in such examples we must recognize the influence of the intelligent mind of man and the work of skilled human hands.

One particular type of Pliocene "eolith" is found at the base of, or beneath, the "Red Crag", Ipswich. It was shaped from a carefully selected piece of flat flint. One end was held between the thumb and forefinger; the other end was chipped until it was shaped like an eagle's beak; from the point of the "beak" the worker formed an edge which we call the "keel".

This little tool has been named the "rostro-carinate" (beak and keel) flint, and, so far, specimens of it have been found in East Anglia only. It may thus have been invented by the early inhabitants of present-day England.

When Early Man had begun to make use of flint he must have searched for the places in which it could be obtained. Experience would teach him in time where to look for the raw material, and he would find it convenient to settle in flint-yielding areas. Indeed, it is in the districts where there is chalk—flint being found chiefly in chalk—that the flint tools of the early hunters are now discovered in largest numbers. Apparently the population in Pliocene times was most dense in chalk districts, just as to-day it is, on the whole, most dense in the districts in which coal and metals are found.

Ancient flint implements are, however, discovered also in districts where there is no chalk, and this fact may be taken as an indication that the workers in flint-yielding areas exchanged their handy tools for other things they required. It is found too that the hunters who lived at a distance from the chalk belts made some use of stones, other than flint, of suitable shapes and sizes and endeavoured to work them as flint was worked. The mind of man was active, and sought out many inventions.

In ancient days, however, the progress made was slow

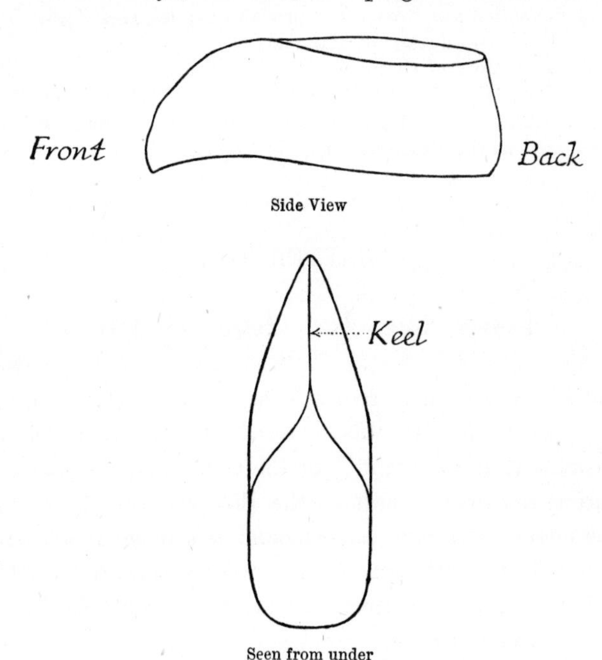

Rostro-carinate Flint Tool (Ideal Form) after Reid Moir

because so much time was occupied in procuring food. Man was surrounded by many perils. Beasts of prey were numerous, and when the animals on which human beings fed grew scarce, there must have been famines and heavy death rates in stricken communities.

Mr. J. Reid Moir's notable discoveries of the "eoliths"

of Early Man in East Anglia are given as follows by Professor Henry Fairfield Osborn of Columbia University, U.S.A.:

(1) Rostro-carinate flints from the base of the Red Crag, Ipswich, or beneath it: of Pliocene Age.
(2) Foxhall flints from the coprolith quarries, near Ipswich: of the Pliocene Age of Mammals.
(3) Giant flints of Cromer, of the early Pleistocene Age of Man, from the Forest bed deposits exposed at the end of the bathing beach below the cliffs of Cromer, of about the same age as the Heidelberg man of Germany.

CHAPTER II

How the Ice Age Began

The Pliocene ("more recent") Age of the Tertiary period of the world's history was followed by the age called the Pleistocene ("most recent") or the Quaternary period.

During the greater part of the Pliocene Age the climate in the country we now call England was much more genial than it is in our own time. There were long warm summers and short and mild winters, and the hunting people did not require to live in caves.

In the deep forests there were trees that now grow only in the south of Europe, and there were also trees that have become extinct as have the huge animals which fed upon their leaves. In the rivers and lakes and on the sea-coasts were shell-fish that are not now found farther north than the Mediterranean area. The shells of these ancient molluscs are, as stated, discovered in Pliocene deposits.

Before the close of the Pliocene Age, however, the climate

in our northern regions began gradually to grow cooler. The winters were then longer and more severe than they had been, and the summers shorter and less warm. Many trees became stunted in growth and hardier trees grew more numerous. The southern molluscs vanished and the big mammals migrated southward. All the apes and monkeys disappeared. It may be that many members of the hunting tribes left the country we know as England.

Early in the Pleistocene Age very severe weather prevailed during the winter. In the spring icebergs drifted down from the north, and, entering the estuaries, choked them so that the rivers flooded and caused much destruction. The hills of the area now called Scotland were capped with snow even in the summer season and small glaciers were being formed. Cold piercing winds blew from the north and east.

The climate grew colder and colder. In the course of centuries great ice-packs pressing down from the Arctic regions gradually covered the countries now called Norway and Sweden, and remained throughout each short summer. The Baltic was frozen over in winter, and the ice ultimately became so thick that it remained unmelted during the whole year. Every winter the ice area extended, until in time it reached and remained in Northern Germany. This was the first phase of the Great Ice Age.

We do not know with certainty what caused the northern ice-field to extend gradually and cover a great part of Northern Europe. Other areas were similarly affected. The glaciers of the Alps grew deeper and longer, as likewise did those of other great mountain ranges through the world. It may be, as some suppose, that great changes were taking place in the sun, that, for some reason which we can only guess at, the supply of heat and light reaching the earth had been reduced.

Scientists tell us that the sun is always changing in our own time, and that the sun spots, which are supposed to be caused by disturbances called "solar storms", increase and decrease in regular cycles. They calculate that if, on account of mysterious solar changes and the obscuring of a part of the sun's surface, there should, for a period of years, be a decrease of only two per cent in the present supply of sunlight, the climate in every part of the world would be greatly altered. "In a few centuries," one writer says of such a change, "it might easily cause the return of the great ice-sheet." On the other hand, an increase of two per cent of solar energy would make some of our northern lands as warm as are the tropical districts at present. Two per cent of the sun's heat, it has been calculated, is about equal to the heat of two million tons of coal burned in a minute or nearly three billion tons burned in a day.

The Great Ice Age was divided into four main periods of different length, and between these there were long and warm inter-glacial periods. It must be borne in mind, however, that the changes of climate did not take place rapidly, but very gradually over prolonged periods of time.

When the earliest phase of the Ice Age, that is, the first glacial epoch, was passing away, the ice-sheet began slowly to shrink in Scandinavia, and each summer great torrents poured down from the hills. Their beds became deeper and deeper and immense quantities of soil were displaced. Owing to the ravages made by floods the natural features of the country were greatly changed.

As the winters grew shorter and milder, the climate of northern Europe greatly improved until it became much warmer than it is now. The First Inter-glacial epoch had been ushered in, and it lasted longer than did the First Glacial epoch.

The earliest known human remains found in England, which are portions of a skull, are believed by some scientists to belong to the First Inter-glacial epoch, but others think they should be regarded as of somewhat later date. The skull is a female one, and the race which it represents has been named "Piltdown" because the find was made in a gravel pit at Piltdown in the Sussex Weald. Some labourers, who were obtaining material from this pit to repair a road, broke and threw away the skull after removing it. It chanced, however, that Mr. Charles Dawson, a well-known scientist, picked up and examined a fragment. He saw that the bone was very thick and that it was fossilized, a sure indication that the skull was a very ancient one.

Searching through the gravel, Mr. Dawson recovered other pieces of the skull. The pit was afterwards turned over and carefully searched, and other relics came to light, including flints resembling eoliths and an implement which has been made from the thigh bone of an elephant and shaped somewhat like a modern cricket bat, with the "handle" end pointed.

Scientists engaged themselves in fitting together the bones of this ancient human head, and although portions were missing, the original form was well suggested. It was found that the thick-skulled members of the Piltdown race had comparatively large and smooth foreheads, but their lower jaws retreated so much that they could not have been very handsome. If, however, they had bright, intelligent eyes their faces may have been quite pleasant.

The well-formed Piltdown skull protruded a good deal at the back, and scientists have found that the brain in this region has more to do with vision and hearing and with storing up memories of things seen and heard, than with thinking and inventing. It may be that Piltdown man was a splendid tracker and excellent hunter. He probably had wonderful

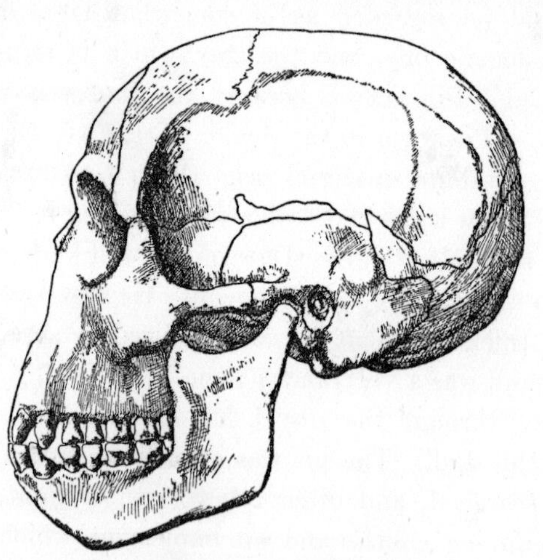

Reconstruction of the Piltdown Skull

By permission of Professor G. Elliot Smith.

vision and could distinguish things at a greater distance than we can, and observe close at hand traces of animals which escape our attention.

One cannot help wondering, however, how Piltdown men and other early hunters were able to kill the big animals on which they fed. Their flints were small and not of much account as weapons. Eoliths could have been used only to scrape flesh off bones, to cut through a slain animal's hide,

TAR POOL SCENE IN THE PLEISTOCENE AGE

From a painting by Charles R. Knight. By courtesy of the Metropolitan Museum of Natural History, New York. See page 24

or to shape tools of wood and bone. Perhaps the bat-shaped bone tool found in the Piltdown gravel pit was fashioned by a worker who used eolithic tools. It may be, on the other hand, that the eoliths were shaped by representatives of a different race.

When we come to consider the facts that have been accumulated regarding the early hunting age of man, it is of very special interest to find that the bones associated with his relics are chiefly those of young animals. Apparently, it was easier to catch and slay young elephants and deer than fully grown ones.

Now, it is well known that wild animals always protect their young and attack furiously any man or beast that interferes with them. When these animals migrate from place to place, and move to and from feeding grounds, the young generally walk in front. Modern hunters tell us that when elephants go down to a river to drink, the young are closely followed by the mothers.

If the primitive hunters had attacked the young animals in the presence of the big ones they would have run serious risks. They must, therefore, have depended on trapping. Perhaps they dug pits which were covered over with branches and grass. The bat-shaped implement of Piltdown may have been a combined pick and spade used for making pits in the sandy river banks.

When a young elephant, being in front of the mother, fell into a pit, the mother would no doubt remain near the pit for a time, and have to be driven away.

The early hunters had no weapons, such as arrows or darts, to hurt and scare big elephants. They could, however, light fires. Burning brands flung at a wild elephant would make it run. If the hunters could not safely venture near enough to an elephant to fling anything at it, they could set the dry grass on fire and thus force it to retreat.

Positive evidence of the use of fire by man has been obtained in connexion with human relics of a later period than that of Piltdown man. It is possible, however, that on account of the severity of the climate, fire was used even before caves were chosen as dwellings.

The important discovery that fire could be made of service to human beings is certainly of great antiquity. In our own day we have much respect and admiration for the inventors who first made use of steam and electricity. These were great men who have conferred priceless benefits on the human race. We should similarly admire the ancient discoverers who first made fire captive and showed how it could be used with safety and to man's advantage not only to give warmth but to scare away beasts of prey.

At first fire may have been obtained from blazing logs at the edge of a forest which had been set in flames by lightning. In time men learned to keep a small fire burning so as to kindle other fires from it. Some savages in our own time keep smouldering logs in their villages, and when these are suddenly extinguished by heavy rain, they go in search of fire. Early man may have done the same.

After fire came into use in ancient times, the next great discovery made was how to produce it. It may be that the busy flint-workers sometimes picked up and used iron pyrites, striking sparks from flint. Then some man with an inventive mind would discover, after experiment, that when he directed showers of sparks into dried grass and leaves he could blow the smouldering parts into flame.

Another discovery of importance was that sparks issued from certain varieties of wood when rubbed together. Perhaps it was made when an artisan was endeavouring to scrape a piece of wood into a tool with a harder piece. The use of "fire-sticks" was then introduced. In time—many centuries later—the "fire-drill" was invented, but, as one can realize, it could never have been thought of until after man had advanced step by step on the path of progress. First he had to use fire, then he had to produce it, and finally he had to find how it could be produced more quickly than before; and, in districts where flint and iron pyrites could not be got, by some other means.

It should not be assumed that because man had many needs he was bound, sooner or later, to satisfy them as a matter of course. He was not really aware, for instance, that he required "fire-sticks" before fire came into use. The path of progress was a hard and tedious one and all peoples did not advance at the same rate or in the same way. There are living in the world to-day backward peoples who have not made much progress during thousands of years.

We owe much to the early thinkers and inventors who introduced many useful things which are to us the commonplaces of daily life. They laid the basis on which the fabric of civilization has been gradually built up.

CHAPTER III

Cold Periods and Warm Periods

The Second Glaciation was a much greater one than the first. It extended over a wider area and it lasted longer. Not only did the Scandinavian ice-field move southward towards Germany as in the First Glacial period but westward towards Britain. The North Sea plain suffered greatly. At first the river mouths were blocked by icebergs that had drifted down from the Arctic and a great deal of flooding took place. Big lakes and marshes were formed and ultimately the plain was completely submerged. Then cold Arctic currents swept southward bringing icebergs which stranded on the coast of modern Norfolk. In time the ice-field crept across the shallow North Sea, and then Scotland, Ireland, and the greater part of England, as far south as the Thames and Severn valleys, were covered with ice which grew thicker and thicker as the centuries went past. The pressure of the "ice pack" was constant and great. Valleys were choked with ice, rivers were frozen solid, and glaciers crept down from the mountains. The great ice-field was pushed gradually westward into the Atlantic area for over fifty miles beyond the present western coasts of the British Isles. If one could have crossed the Atlantic Ocean from America during the period of the Second Glaciation, one would have seen great cliffs of ice several hundreds of feet high stretching far to the west of the British Isles.

Scotland then resembled the regions round the North Pole. The ice-sheet that lay upon it was so thick that only the white tops of the highest mountains could be seen. At the present time one can find ice-scratchings on the mountains of western Ross-shire to a height of about 3500 feet, but in the Outer Hebrides the marks left by the ice are not found much higher than about 1550 feet. It would seem, therefore, that the great ice-fields sloped gradually downward from the mountains of western Scotland towards the "ice-cliffs" in the Atlantic. From these ice-cliffs big icebergs drifted southward, carrying boulders that had been carried down from the Scottish hills by great glaciers. These ice-borne boulders are called "erratics", and some of them were stranded on the Azores where the icebergs gradually melted.

From Scandinavia the ice-field was pushed southward across the Baltic and eastward across the Ural mountains. The greater part of Russia was covered with ice. Modern Denmark, Holland, and Belgium were completely buried. It has been found that in Denmark the ice was 2500 feet thick. The ice-field covered much of modern Germany, and in the Berlin area was about 1300 feet thick. In Norway there were "mountains of ice" to the height of about 7000 feet. When the ice-field moved eastward across Europe its progress was arrested by the Carpathian Mountains.

In central Europe the Alpine ice-field stretched northward to the Jura Mountains, eastward to the outskirts of modern Vienna, westward to the edge of the Rhone valley in France and southward into northern Italy. Glaciers crept down the mountains of France, and a thick and heavy ice-field stretched out from the Pyrenees into modern France and Spain. Even the Sierra Nevada range in southern Spain had its glaciers, as had also the Atlas Mountains in Morocco.

Italy had a severe climate. There were small glaciers in

the Apennines. Along the northern shores of the Mediterranean Sea were molluscs that nowadays are found only in the North Atlantic. Egypt was not then a hot country, but it had a pleasant climate and much rain fell. Thick forests flourished between the Nile and the Red Sea and the present Sahara desert had grassy plains, wooded hills, lakes, and rivers.

There were great masses of ice in Asia Minor, and northern Asia was covered with ice like northern Europe. The high mountain ranges of central Asia were also ice-fields, and thin glaciers moved over wide areas. Canada and the northern parts of the United States lay under ice. Traces of the ancient glaciers still remain near modern New York. The Rocky Mountains had long and heavy glaciers. There were ice-sheets also in South America. The higher parts of the Australian, Tasmanian, and New Zealand mountains were covered with ice.

The great changes which took place all over the world during the Second Glaciation were brought about very slowly and over a vast period of time. Century after century the climate grew colder and colder. Then, after the limit of glaciation had been reached everywhere, the winters gradually grew milder and shorter, and the summers grew longer and warmer. In the course of time the various ice-fields began to retreat. Great floods were caused when the ice-fields were melting. Rivers were swollen heavily and roared in the valleys, which were cut and torn deeply. Big lakes and wide marshes were formed in areas which are nowadays covered with forests and farms, cities and towns and villages.

Many centuries went past, and then came on very gradually the warm Second Inter-glacial period—the longest of all the periods of the Pleistocene Age. To realize how long the period was, it may be explained that it was followed in turn by the Third Glacial period, and then the Fourth Glacial period, which was the last. The Second Inter-glacial period was longer than the entire period from the beginning of the Third Glacial period till the present time. One estimate of its length is 200,000 years.

At the beginning of this Second Inter-glacial period the land gradually rose. The cause of this change is not definitely known, but some scientists suggest that the great burden of ice which had lain for many centuries on a large portion of land had caused it to sink, and that when the ice melted the land rose like a sponge which has been pressed down by one's hand and then released.

When the land rose, the North Sea plain was restored, as was also the valley of the English Channel. The land movement was not, however, confined to the northern area. Italy was once again united with North Africa so that the Mediterranean Sea was cut into two. Europe was connected with North America, which stretched from the north of present-day Scotland to Iceland and Greenland, while Asia was connected with North America by a "land-bridge" stretching across the present Bering Straits.

Europe having grown warmer—much warmer than it is nowadays—large forests flourished far and wide. Warmth-loving animals from Africa and Asia wandered into our forests, reaching as far as present-day Britain. These included the broad-nosed rhinoceros with two horns, and the big hippopotamus. There were two types of elephants—the gigantic southern mammoth and the straight-tusked elephant. The ferocious sabre-tusked tigers returned to the haunts of their ancestors but were not so numerous as formerly. There were, however, a good many African lions in Europe.

The beasts of prey found plenty of food. Herds of wild horses grazed on hill slopes and on the plains, and there were herds of bison and wild cattle. In the forests were various types of deer, from the little roe-deer to the giant deer and the big moose with its flat broad face and massive antlers. Bears, wild pigs, wolves, big wild cats, and beavers, as well as a great variety of birds, were to be found in Europe, and there were many reptiles, including big serpents.

Human beings lived in Europe during this warm Second Inter-glacial period. They were of different races, but, as they lived in the open, and not in caves as at a later period, few remains of them have been found. A heavy human jaw was discovered in 1907 at a depth of about 78 feet in a sand-pit at Mauer, near Heidelberg in Germany. Near this ancient relic were found the bones of some of the beasts of prey that lived in Europe during the long Second Inter-glacial period. Little can be said about "Heidelberg man" (as he is called), except that he must have differed from the Piltdown man. His jaw suggests that he was of very powerful build. It may be, indeed, as some think, that he used his jaw like a tool to kill and tear as do some of the modern Australian savages. We do not know whether or not he worked flint. It may be that he was not of so high a type as Piltdown man, but resembled more closely a later race, which differed very much from the early hunters with nimble fingers and large foreheads who lived in the area known as East Anglia.

Another type of man who seems to have lived during the Second Inter-glacial period is represented by a skull called after Galley Hill in Kent, where it was found in a gravel pit in 1888. " Galley Hill " man, as he is known to scientists, had a large brain, and resembled modern man more closely than did Piltdown man.

CHAPTER IV

Ancient Animals in Asphalt and Ice

When the early hunters were living in the country we now call England, there may have been similar types of human beings in North America, but no traces of them have yet been found. There were, however, numerous animals and reptiles, and when the ice-sheet crept southward from the Arctic regions they were forced to retreat before it.

In the modern state of California the skeletons of hundreds of early Pleistocene animals have been discovered in a wonderful state of preservation. The region is rich in oil, which here and there bubbles up to the surface of the ground, forming what are known as " tar pools ". Some of the pools which existed in Pleistocene times have long been hardened into asphalt " beds " and modern pools have formed near them. In these beds are found the bones of extinct animals, many skeletons being quite complete.

One famous tar-pool area in California bears the Spanish name of Rancho-la-Brea (" Ranch of the Tar Pools "). The existing pools are surrounded with cactus and trees and covered with thin sheets of water. If a wild animal is tempted to drink from one of them, it runs the risk of being caught in the tar and when that happens it perishes miserably, for it is gradually sucked down by the liquid and smothered.

During the early part of the Ice Age, when the surrounding mountains were covered with snow, large numbers of animals were entrapped in the ancient "tar pools". The least intelligent, including the bison, the sloth, and the American camel, were the most common victims. Wild horses were caught occasionally. In a single asphalt pit were found the bones of no fewer than seventeen elephants, but these had not all perished at the same time, because the ancient pool was comparatively small. Greedy beasts of prey often perished in the ancient "tar pools". The big wolf is well represented among the finds. Apparently, when an elephant or horse was caught in a pool, its cries of distress attracted prowling packs of wolves which leapt at the poor victim, only, however, to be themselves caught in the tar from which they could not possibly escape.

Tragedies of this kind were numerous, and occasionally there were fierce conflicts at the pools between the larger and stronger animals. Mr. Charles R. Knight, an American artist, has recently painted a vigorous picture of a tar-pool scene in the Pleistocene Age. He undertook this interesting work after making a close study of the numerous skeletons of the extinct animals which have been recovered from the asphalt pits of Rancho-la-Brea. The substance in which they lay has preserved even the fragile bones of birds.

The picture shows a snarling sloth with its legs securely caught in a tar pool. Two other sloths have come to its assistance in response to its cries of alarm. On the opposite side of the pool is a fierce sabre-toothed tiger with jaws a-gape, ready to spring at the entrapped victim. The three sloths are growling angry defiance, and the two which are free have risen on their hind legs to fight with their long curving claws, which are powerful weapons. A second sabre-toothed tiger comes up to take part in the battle, and on the branches of a tree near the pool are vultures waiting patiently to feast on the bodies of any of the animals which are killed and partly devoured.

One can tell from a glance at the picture what is to happen as soon as the fight begins. The sabre-toothed tiger which is to leap at the sloth in the pool will itself be caught in the tar, and the same fate awaits the other tiger and the two sloths on the bank which are rearing to receive the tigers.

After the struggling animals have fought their last fight and, torn and bleeding, sink exhausted in the treacherous tar, the vultures will pounce upon their bodies and begin to gorge themselves. They, too, will perish, however, for the tar will smear their wings and claws and make it impossible for them to escape. Other vultures flying through the air are likely to become victims also.

In the background is a herd of gigantic elephants. These animals have paused as if scared by the snarling tigers and howling sloths, and seem to be about to turn towards another water-covered tar pool to slake their thirst. At least one of them is sure to become a helpless victim.

In an American museum some of the skeletons of Pleistocene animals have been set up so as to illustrate how they perished in one of these terrible pools of tar. A gigantic sloth is shown lying in the pool. Over it, with its mouth agape, stoops a tiger whose legs are sunk in the tar, and on the bank crouches a big wolf which fears to approach the tiger so long as it is able to growl, but it will leap down when that fierce animal becomes silent, and it, too, will be caught in the tar, from which it cannot possibly escape.

At McKittrick, about 120 miles distant from Rancho-la-Brea, large numbers of birds were entrapped in the tar pools which were covered with thin sheets of water. Flocks of ducks and geese flying from a distance descended to the pools without the least suspicion of danger, and never rose from them again. Herons, storks, and cranes wandered into them and were caught as securely as they might have been in snares. Pigeons, doves, quails, cuckoos, swallows, larks, plovers, crows, ravens, and other passing birds went to drink at the pools and never were seen again. Then birds of prey, seeing ducks, geese, &c., struggling in the tar, pounced down to seize the victims and they themselves were entrapped.

These tar pools, in which so many animals met their doom, have preserved for us valuable evidence regarding early Pleistocene times. Scientists are enabled to make a close study of the bones of extinct animals, and also to throw light on the migrations of those animals. The giant mammoth, which became a victim in a Rancho-la-Brea tar pool, was, for instance, a type which had wandered into America from southern Asia. The ground cuckoo came from the same area. Other animals had crossed into America by the land-bridge which connected that continent with north-eastern Asia. The sloths had migrated northward from South America. A specially interesting animal was the Pleistocene American camel. It differed from the true camel of Asia and from the llama of South America. Scientists regard it as a link between these two animal types. Most of the beasts of prey were common to North America and northern Asia. The wild horses were numerous along the Pacific coast of the American continent, but they disappeared during the last stage of the Ice Age.

Some of the animals which were trapped were forest-lovers. Their presence in the hardened substance of the ancient tar pools gives us clues as to the climate in which they lived. When the American camels were preyed upon by the American lions in southern California, there were wide grass-lands and clumps of forest in which tapirs and elephants and sloths prowled about. The trunk of a cypress tree was found in one of the hardened " beds ". Apparently a tar pool bubbled up through its roots and it was gradually sucked down into its depths as the pool grew deeper and wider.

When the Ice Age was at its height, the winters became severe and long and the summers comparatively cold and short. Many trees perished and others were stunted in growth. The grass-lands were frozen and ruined as feeding-grounds for the greater part of each year. Deprived of their food-supply, the herds of wild animals that fed in forests and on plains were forced to migrate and many became extinct, as did the wild horses. Many carnivorous animals that preyed upon them perished also.

The story of the Ice Age is in every part of the world a tragic story.

In northern Asia the bodies of ancient mammoths, which perished miserably owing to the intense cold and the scarcity of food, have been found embedded in cliffs of " fossil ice ". These great animals had been in the habit of browsing on the willows and alders that grew round inland lakes and on the banks of rivers, and as the winters grew longer, they found it more and more difficult to keep up the struggle for existence. Some were frozen to death during the winter, and the ice then formed round their bodies. Hundreds of years went past and the ice did not melt.

When milder weather came on, the ice, which in some places formed thick cliffs, was covered over with loam and sand, which protected the dense and hard masses from the heat of the short summer suns.

Thousands of years went past and the ancient beds of ice were covered over with sand and snow and fresh ice. The bodies of the frozen mammoths remained in a state of wonderful preservation. In some places the cliffs of fossil ice have remained until our own time, towering to a height of from 50 to 70 feet.

A number of frozen mammoths have been discovered on the New Siberian islands. Occasionally during a warm summer a huge block of ice is splintered and a mammoth's body is laid bare. The sailors and fishermen on the Siberian coast have for many years searched for frozen mammoths so as to obtain their great tusks of ivory and sell them to traders.

In 1799 a party of men in quest of mammoth ivory saw in a large block of ice on one of the New Siberian islands a big dark form which they suspected to be a mammoth. It was too deeply embedded to be reached, and the ancient ice was almost as hard as stone. They returned next summer and observed that a good deal of the ancient ice had melted. It was evident that the animal would in time be laid bare. When the third summer came round they could see through the ice the crouching form of the mammoth and one of its big curving tusks. It was not, however, until the fifth summer that the body of the ancient animal was released. The lower part of the ice had melted so much that the whole mass was split asunder owing to the weight of the monster. Then a part slipped away, as does an iceberg from an Arctic ice-sheet, and, tumbling on to the beach, it broke open. The body of the big mammoth was thus laid bare.

It had been kept in "cold storage" for thousands of years, and the flesh was so well preserved that the men and their dogs devoured it freely. When they went away bears and other wild animals scented the carcass and came to feast on it, and the sea-birds gathered in large numbers to gorge on the flesh and fat.

In 1806 the carcass was found by English sailors and their discovery was made known to the Russian authorities. It was then decided to remove what was left of the ancient mammoth to a museum in St. Petersburg. The entire skeleton was intact, and large portions of the skin remained and were seen to be covered with a furry wool of reddish colour, interspersed with black hairs. The animal, which had been nearly twice the size of a modern elephant, was carefully stuffed and set up in the Royal museum in the crouching position in which it had been originally found.

In 1860 a Russian who hunted regularly for mammoth ivory discovered a frozen mammoth in a deep crevice of fossil ice which had long been covered over with sand, peat, and loam. The animal was in an upright position and in a fine state of preservation. Three years later there was a "rock slide" and the mammoth's body slipped from the crevice. It tumbled down to the beach, and unfortunately was carried away to sea.

A geologist who examined the site where this mammoth had been preserved for thousands of years, found that the ancient ice had first been covered with a layer of sand. Above this was a layer of peat; then came layers of loam and thin ice, and above these were the deposits of recent times. These layers had for centuries and centuries prevented the sun's rays and heat from reaching the fossil ice and melting it.

The late Professor James Geikie tells that "even at the present day the drifted snows in south-east Russia are occasionally buried under sands and so persist for years". He notes, in illustration of this, that a Russian geologist once came across what appeared to be an ordinary sandhill, but "it proved to be a mass of congealed snow cloaked in sand about a foot in thickness". Immediately under the sand layer the snow was powdery, "but a little deeper it was firm and solid ice".

Occasionally heaps of bones of various kinds of ancient animals are found embedded in sandy loam, and it is possible these are the remains of the victims of prehistoric snowstorms. When a blizzard came on, the animals sought shelter in the lee of a hill. There they were buried and smothered in the snow, and afterwards the congealed snow was covered over with masses of drifting sand, or by stones and earth that slipped down the hillside.

Among the heaps of animal remains that have been dug out in different parts of Europe, it is found that beasts of prey and vegetation-feeding animals perished together. When faced by a common danger, such as a sudden and blinding snow-blizzard, the animals ceased to attack or flee from one another. They gathered together for mutual protection and warmth, the deer beside the lion, the wolf beside the wild ox, and together they perished from cold and starvation.

SKELETONS OF PLEISTOCENE ANIMALS AT THE TAR POOL

By courtesy of the American Museum of Natural History, New York. See page 25

CHAPTER V

Types of Ice-Age Men

The tools of early man of the Stone Age have been arranged in three main classes. These are (1) the Eoliths ("dawn stones"), (2) the Palæoliths ("old stones"), and (3) the Neoliths ("new stones").

As we have seen, the Eoliths were shaped by the earliest hunters who made use of flint. These hunters lived from Pliocene times, the last stage of the Tertiary period, till the Chellean flints came into use. These Chellean tools are the earliest Palæoliths, and they have been named after Chelles, near Paris, where those first recognized were found. The Neoliths were invented after the climate of Europe became similar to what it is now—that is, at the beginning of the Modern Age.

In Chapter III we dealt with the types of human beings who were in Europe during the Second Glacial period. They must have been forced to retreat southward when the Third Glacial period came on.

Once again the climate grew gradually colder, until Scandinavia was completely covered with ice. The heavy ice-sheet spread southward to northern Germany and across the North Sea area to Britain, but a greater part of England was left bare than during the Second Glacial period, for the ice-sheet did not come much farther south than Yorkshire; southern Wales and southern Ireland were also free of ice. In the river valleys of France and Spain the summers were comparatively mild, but the winters were cold—not cold enough, apparently, to force human beings to live in caves. Perhaps the ancient men could resist the cold much better than we do.

Next came on the Third Inter-glacial period, in which so many human relics have been found that we obtain vivid glimpses of man's life and progress. The Palæoliths were shaped in large numbers. There were various types of these, but the chief was a massive tool which was held in the hand, and has been named the Chellean. The men who made use of this tool must have been brave and bold hunters.

The Chellean hand-axe (called by the French the *coup de poing*) was shaped somewhat like a pear, one end being thick so that it might be firmly gripped. The edge and point were carefully chipped so that it might serve the double purpose of a lance and an axe. With it the hunters could kill and cut up animals and also shape tools from wood and bone.

The later "hand axes" are found to be more carefully shaped than the earlier. They were made neater and the edge was extended. Other Chellean tools are called "choppers", "scrapers", &c. We can only make guesses as to what uses these tools served.

When the weather was growing colder because the Fourth Glacial stage was coming on, the working of flint improved greatly. The new industry was either developed by the men who had been living in western Europe for many centuries, or was introduced by hunters from some other area. New types of tools came into use and these are called the Acheulian, after St. Acheul in the Somme valley, France, where typical specimens were first identified. A keener edge was obtained by the deft secondary flaking of the flints. The edge was rendered sharper by being carefully worked over again by pressure with a bone or wooden tool. " Hand axes " were made smaller and in different forms, as if to suit different purposes. Some of the tools were really " hand knives ", others were " hand lances " with sharp points, and others were probably used for scraping and boring.

The Chellean and Acheulian tools have been found in

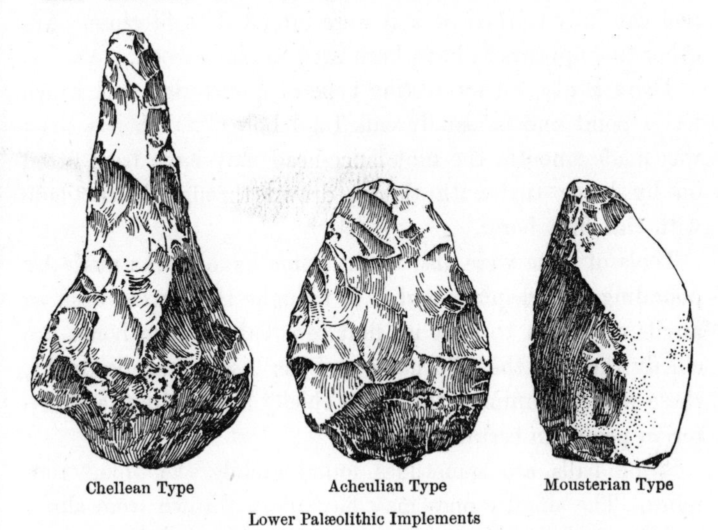

Chellean Type Acheulian Type Mousterian Type

Lower Palæolithic Implements

England chiefly in the valleys of the Thames and the Ouse and in the " Pinhole cave " at Cresswell Crags, Derbyshire, but not in Wales, Scotland, and Ireland. When Acheulian man was in England the commonest animals were the reindeer and the hairy mammoths.

The next class of Palæoliths is the Mousterian, named after Le Moustier in the valley of the River Vézère in France.

The Mousterian industry was a new one in Western Europe.

It was introduced towards the end of the Third Inter-glacial period and lasted all through the Fourth Glacial period, that is, for many thousands of years.

An interesting fact about the Mousterian tools is that they were shaped not from cores of flint but from the sharp flakes. A pointed blade, which was favoured, seems to have been attached to a wooden shaft, because the base is broad and carefully worked as if it were intended to fit close. Another tool appears to have been used to plane wood.

There is also an interesting type of Mousterian tool which has a point and is usually called a " borer ". When a shaft was made smooth, the flint lance-head may have been fitted on by being tied with thongs drawn through holes made with this flint borer.

Tools of bone were also used. Some have marks made by pounding and rasping, and it is thought these were used as anvils on which to split up flint into flakes. The bones are chiefly those of the wild horse and the bison, and, no doubt, these were the animals that were chiefly hunted by the Mousterian people in certain areas.

Stone balls are sometimes found among the Mousterian relics. The smaller ones may have been thrown from slings and the larger ones may have been enclosed in hide bags, to which thongs were attached, and used to kill animals caught in pits or traps.

The Mousterian tools were not so finely made as the earlier Acheulian ones, nor were they so varied. There was a very special reason for this. Mousterian man differed very much from Piltdown man, who worked small flints, and from Chellean man, who gripped a flint axe in his hand. He belonged to a very powerful but clumsy-looking race. Although he had

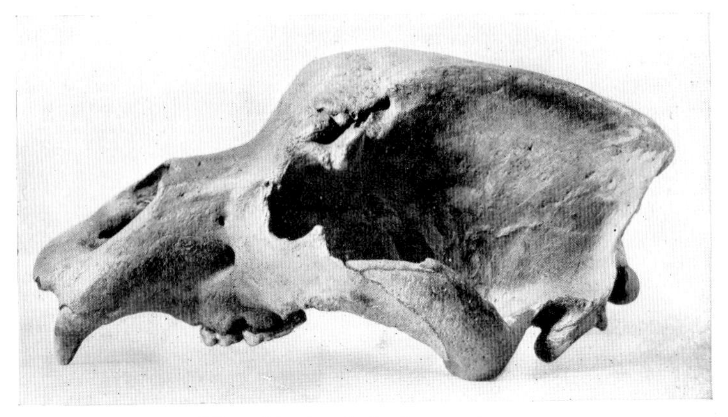

Wound in the skull of a cave-bear

Rock polished by the fur of cave-bears

REMAINS OF CAVE-BEARS IN THE DRAGON'S CAVE NEAR MIXNITZ, AUSTRIA

By permission of Othenio Abel, from photographs lent by the American Museum of Natural History, New York

big strong hands, they were not so nimble as those of the earlier peoples who inhabited western Europe and the area known as England.

If we were to catch a glimpse of a company of Mousterian hunters crossing the English Channel valley towards modern Kent, we should be inclined to smile at them. The men were small, the tallest being no more than 5 feet 5 inches in height, and the women were under 5 feet. They walked with a stoop, their big heads being thrust forward and their knees were always bent. They could not run or stand like a modern man. Their necks were so short and thick that when they looked sideways they turned not only their heads but also the upper parts of their bodies. They had very broad shoulders and their arms were short but very muscular. If we could have seen these hunters we should have noticed as they came closer that their faces were very ugly. Their foreheads were low and retreating and a bony ridge jutted out above their eyes, their noses were broad and coarse and their mouths very large, while their chins fell back towards their throats.

Their fingers were very short and broad, and they had such stiff thumbs that they could not be moved nimbly across and up and down the inside of the hand. Indeed, they could be bent as far backward as forward. When they gripped a small object they did so by pressing the thumb sideways against the first finger. They thus held a flint tool pretty much as we hold a pen, but with thumb and forefinger held straighter. As their fingers were strong, if not supple, they could use a scraper, a planer, or a borer quite freely, and they could grasp firmly, if in an awkward fashion, a stout shaft of a flint-headed lance.

Mousterian man is also called Neanderthal man. The

latter name has been given after Neanderthal, near Düsseldorf, in Germany, where a fairly complete skeleton of the human species was found in 1857. Another skeleton was afterwards found at La Chapelle-aux-Saints in France. Skulls of Neanderthal man which have been discovered are named after their localities and include the Spy skull No. 1, the Gibraltar skull, the Krapina skull, &c.

The Neanderthal people lived in Europe all through the Fourth Glacial period, when the Scandinavian ice-sheet once again extended gradually over a great part of northern Europe. The land sank and the North Sea plain disappeared and the sea poured into the English Channel valley. The country we know as England was then very much as is Spitzbergen at the present time, and in France, which had a climate resembling that of northern Siberia nowadays, there lived the reindeer and hairy mammoth. In Wales, Scotland, and Ireland the ice-fields were not so extensive as they had been in the Second and Third Glacial periods, but still the winters must have been very severe. In some areas the glaciers melted in the summer before reaching the sea.

The Mousterian hunters who came to the country we know as England reached as far north as Derbyshire. Some of their relics have been found in the "Pinhole cave" at Cresswell Crags. They must have crossed over from the country we know as France before the English Channel land-bridge was severed, or when, as a narrow channel, it was completely frozen over.

CHAPTER VI

Brave Hunters of Cave-Bears

The Neanderthal hunters who used Mousterian tools were cave-dwellers. Some scientists are of opinion, however, that when they first arrived in the country we now know as France, the climate was so genial that they were able to live in the open. In the Somme valley their stone tools have been found mingled with the bones of warmth-loving animals like the straight-tusked elephant, the hippopotamus, and the broad-nosed rhinoceros. Other scientists suggest that the bones and tools were carried down by floods from different sites belonging to different periods to the places in which they have been found. In the Thames valley, however, the plant-remains of a temperate climate are associated with some of the relics of Neanderthal man.

Before the hunters used them the caves were the lairs of ferocious wild animals such as the cave-lion, the cave-bear, and the cave-hyæna. In one French cave the bones of no fewer than eight hundred cave-bears have been discovered beneath the tools and weapons of the Neanderthal hunters.

Before making a cave their home, a Neanderthal family had first to clear it of wild beasts. As they made use of fire, they would be able to smoke out the monsters, and fires could afterwards be lit in front of the caves to prevent them returning during the night-time. It has been suggested that the hunters may occasionally have erected stone walls to narrow the entrances of caves, so that they might be better able to secure themselves against attacks by beasts of prey which might be attracted by the scent of meat stored by the hunters.

Modern artists have drawn imaginary pictures of battles waged by the Neanderthals against the gigantic cave-bears. They show these fierce animals snarling angrily at the hunters, who, perched on ledges of rock, throw or roll down big boulders to scare or kill them. Of late, however, fresh discoveries reveal the interesting fact that the ancient hunters were less afraid of the bears than used to be thought, and that they displayed cunning and intelligence in attacking them. The Neanderthals had, it appears, learned by experience that a powerful blow on a bear's muzzle either stunned it or caused instant death, and they made use of their knowledge with much daring and courage. Bears' flesh is quite good to eat. Modern hunters are known to roast "grizzly steaks" and eat them with relish. The Neanderthals not only attacked the cave-bears so as to get possession of their lairs, but also killed them for food.

A wonderful story of the experiences and customs of the ancient hunters has been unfolded of late by a party of Continental scientists. In the "Dragon's Cave" near Mixnitz in Austria the relics of the Neanderthals have been found mingled with the bones of cave-bears, and it has been shown that the men were more than a match for the wild animals.

For centuries it has been known that large quantities of big bones were lying in the cave mingled with dust and bat guano. The people in the neighbourhood used to believe that the bones were those of ancient dragons, unicorns, &c., about which curious "fairy stories" were told. Inside the cave may still be seen on rock faces the inscriptions made by visitors as far back as 1418. They had gone to the cave to procure the wonderful bones, believing them to be those of fabulous monsters, so that they might use them for medicinal purposes. Ground " dragon-bones " were supposed to cure various diseases.

The cave is a large one. It opens in Rötelstein mountain on the Mur river in Styria at a height of over 3000 feet above sea-level, and is about 700 yards in depth. Falls of rock from the roof took place during the Ice Age, dividing the cave into three sections. At a great depth—about 350 yards from the entrance—an earlier fall of rock left only a narrow passage to the dark innermost recess.

Bears are hibernating animals, and in Mousterian times the big cave-bears crept through the narrow passage to the end of the cave to sleep during the coldest months. They had to walk in single file, feeling their way in the darkness, between the blocks of fallen rock. The scientists, using their electric torches, have found that rock-faces have been worn smooth and polished by the furs of countless bears which for many centuries had been in the habit of passing up and down the narrow passage leading to the innermost recess.

At the mouth of this passage two ancient hearths were laid bare. These had been constructed and used by the Neanderthal hunters, who had selected suitable flat slabs of limestone for the purpose. The first hearth lay on the cave floor. It had been in use for a considerable time but ultimately became buried in debris. Apparently the cave was deserted for a period. Other hunters entered it in time, however, and they laid a new limestone fire-hearth above the old one.

The slabs were found to be strewn with dust, charcoal, and Mousterian tools and flakes. The implements were all of quartzite which had been carried into the cave from the river valley. Evidently the Neanderthal hunters had been in the habit of chipping their stone tools as they squatted around the blazing cave fire which gave them light as well as warmth.

The bones of bears scattered on the hearths indicate that those animals were slain and eaten. Not only did the hunters cook the flesh, but they also roasted the bones and then broke them to procure the marrow. Further evidence of the ancient feasts was obtained when the explorers found in a side recess of the cave about thirty skulls of cave-bears lying side by side and hundreds of bears' bones and teeth. Some of the skulls bore marks of wounds that had healed before the animals were finally killed, and one had a wound which had suppurated for some time without healing. All the wounds were on the left sides of the skulls and had been caused by sharp instruments like the quartzite implements on the hearths.

The scientists were amazed to find that the big bears had been attacked in the depths of the cave by the fearless and cunning Neanderthal hunters. Traces of the ancient conflicts still survive. In the narrow passage leading to the innermost recess there is a great block of stone, and opposite it is a wall of soft rock on which there are many deep scratches made by the claws of the powerful animals as they struggled to escape.

When the bears came down the narrow passage from the innermost recess, the rock-face with the scratches was on their right and the great block of stone on their left. As has been stated, the wounds received by the bears were all on the left sides of their heads. The Neanderthal hunters stood on the block of stone and, as the bears came down the narrow passage, they struck fierce and powerful blows at their muzzles either with sling-weapons or with quartzite axes attached with thongs to horn or wooden handles.

If a bear ducked its head, it was wounded on the skull and might escape, the wound healing later. Some of the bears reared themselves on their hind legs and scratched excitedly on the rock-face in their endeavours to find a way of escape. Probably some showed fight and mauled the hunters. The struggle was, however, one of brain against brute force. The Neanderthals not only used their weapons with skill and intelligence, striking at the bears' muzzles, as do modern Slovakians who hunt brown bears in the Carpathian Mountains, but they also made use of fire. Burning brands thrust at the rearing bears must have dazzled and scared them. One hunter may have carried the brands to give light to his companion who struck blows, and he probably used them against an animal which showed fight.

As the fire hearths were placed at the entrance of the narrow passage, it is possible that the hunters lit big fires to arouse the bears from the state of torpor in which they lay during the winter. The smoke probably forced the big animals to come out, gasping and half stupefied. Their human enemies probably terrified them greatly in that deep and dark cave.

The courageous Neanderthal hunters must have had exciting experiences. A snarling bear at bay is a dangerous enemy, and the bears which the Neanderthals attacked so boldly were very much larger than are modern bears. "When," says a writer, "a skull of the cave-bear is placed for comparison alongside one of the grizzly bear of the Rocky Mountains, the latter looks a perfect pigmy."

The ancient hunters who so boldly attacked the bears in the deep cave were ever in danger of being ripped by the claws of the monsters; a single blow from a bear's paw would cause a terrible wound, or, perhaps, instant death. No form of big-game hunting at the present day is more perilous than were those cave-bear hunting exploits of Neanderthal man in far-off times.

The thirty skulls of bears found in its recess had been piled up there either by the hunters or by the action of water. One of the skulls was found, however, to have been securely fixed, with the aid of a leg bone, in a fissure of rock. This could not have been due to an accident. Apparently the skull and bone had been placed in position by human hands and for a very definite reason. It is possible, as has been suggested, that the ancient hunters observed some sort of ceremony with the skulls of the animals they had slain.

The Ainus of Japan, who hunt bears, preserve and venerate the skulls of these animals. Other peoples are known to have observed a similar custom. Tacitus, the Roman historian, tells that the ancient Germans hung up on trees in their sacred groves the heads of certain animals. In England and Scotland the heads of stags, &c., are still preserved, but the custom has lost its ancient meaning. Heads of foxes, as well as horse-shoes, used to be nailed to stable doors to keep out witches; nowadays those who preserve an old horse-shoe say it is "lucky" to do so. A stag's head, placed on the head of a spear, was in former times carried with much ceremony into a church in Essex. Boars' heads were also used in ancient English ceremonies which had lost their original pagan meaning and were kept up simply as "customs". Many peoples in different parts of the world are known to show special

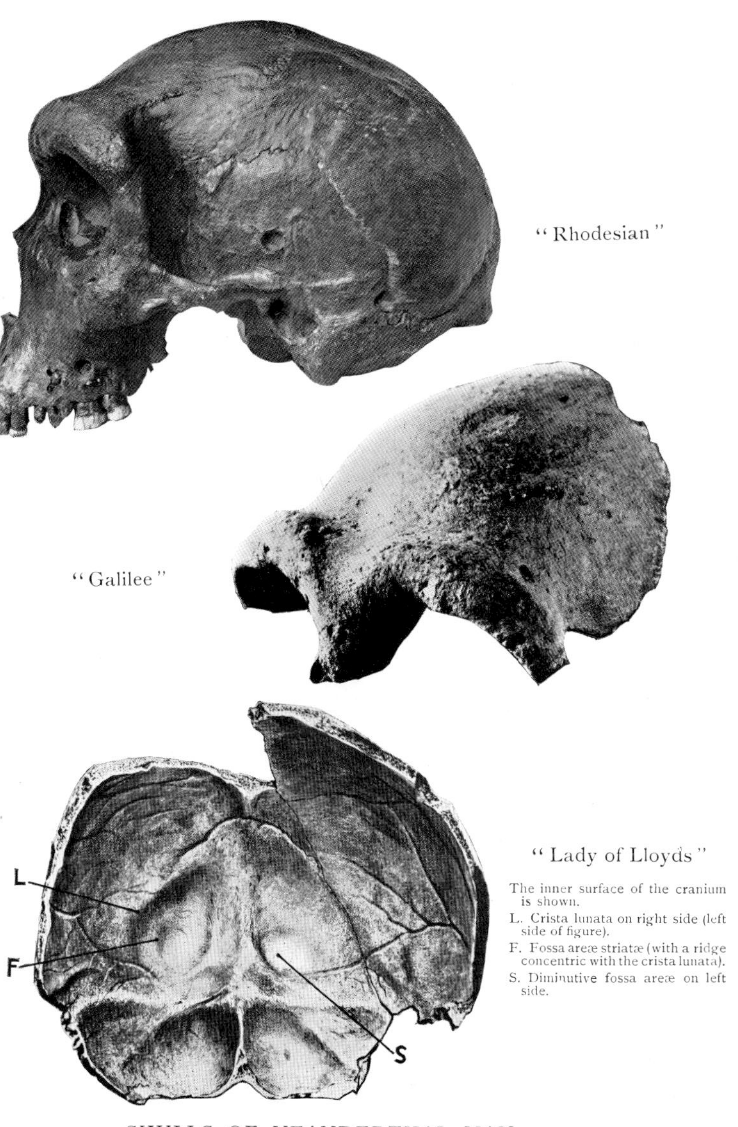

The inner surface of the cranium is shown.

L. Crista lunata on right side (left side of figure).

F. Fossa areæ striatæ (with a ridge concentric with the crista lunata).

S. Diminutive fossa areæ on left side.

SKULLS OF NEANDERTHAL MAN

By permission of the British Museum (Natural History), Professor Elliot Smith, M.D., F.R.S., the British School of Archæology in Jerusalem, and Mr. F. Turville-Petre

reverence for the heads of animals killed by hunters or sacrificed by priests.

The custom of preserving the skulls of animals is of very great antiquity. It was observed not only by the Neanderthal hunters, but by those who came immediately after them during the Post-glacial period.

CHAPTER VII

Ancient Natives of Galilee and London

Two important discoveries of human relics of Palæolithic times were made in 1925—the one in a lonely ravine in Palestine and the other in the midst of populous London. The first was the fairly complete skull of "Galilee man" and the second portions of the skull of the so-called "Lady of Lloyds".

The discoverer of the "Galilee skull" was Mr. F. Turville-Petre. After finishing his studies in Oxford University, this young anthropologist went out to Palestine to take part in the organized work of exploring ancient sites which is conducted by the British School of Archæology in Jerusalem. He travelled north from the city of David and Solomon to the plain of Gennesaret, which skirts the western shore of the Lake of Galilee and is surrounded by barren hills, and there he began his search for antiquities.

Not far from the famous lake is a deep rocky ravine, the cliffs on one side of which rise to a height of about two hundred feet. Some two hundred yards from the entrance to the ravine is a big cave which the natives know as the

"Robbers' Cave", because it was formerly occupied by fierce brigands.

Mr. Turville-Petre decided to explore the ravine. The Robbers' Cave interested him very much, and when he entered it, he observed that the floor was covered with a thick deposit of hardened earth and debris. He decided to have the place explored for relics of ancient times.

At first a trench was dug so that an idea might be obtained as to what sort of relics the cave deposit contained. The workers, who were overlooked by Mr. Turville-Petre, had not dug down more than four feet when it was found that the relics were thousands of years old, and that they had never been disturbed. The cave had been occupied at intervals by human beings back to the time when metals were unknown and tools were made of stone and bone.

Under the four-foot level there was a layer of rock fragments which did not contain a single human relic. Severe winter frosts had in very ancient times split the roof and sides of the cave, the ice acting like wedges, and the portions of rock which had been dislodged fell down on all sides. A long cold period went past, during which no human beings lived in the cave.

Under the rock fragments was a layer of red earth which was about three feet thick. It had been formed by the dust which for many long centuries had been blown into the cave. In this layer were human relics in the form of tools of stone of the type which French archæologists have named Mousterian.

In Europe Mousterian tools belong chiefly to the Fourth Glacial epoch, and it has been proved that they were made and used by the Neanderthal race of hunters. Similar relics had previously been discovered in Palestine, but none of them was associated with human bones, so that there was no direct evidence to show whether or not they were the handiwork of the Neanderthal peoples. In consequence, some scientists were inclined to doubt if Neanderthal man had ever lived in Asia.

When Mr. Turville-Petre reported to the British School of Archæology in Jerusalem that he had made so interesting a discovery in the Robbers' Cave, it was decided that he should continue his work there. The cave deposits were then systematically cleared out and carefully examined.

In the red earth containing Mousterian tools were found the bones of various animals which had been hunted and eaten by men. Some of these animals have long been extinct. There were traces also of ancient fires on which the hunters had cooked flesh and roasted marrow-bones, and there were fragments of flint which had been chipped off the tools that the hunters made and used.

At the very bottom of the red earth layer portions of a human skull were discovered. When these were examined and fitted together it became apparent that, as Sir Arthur Keith has shown, the Mousterian tools in the Robbers' Cave had been shaped by Neanderthal men. The skull was that of a young adult of the Neanderthal race who had been buried in the cave by his friends.

This skull proves that the Neanderthal hunters had lived in Palestine as well as in western Europe. To distinguish this eastern or Asiatic branch of this ancient race, the skull is referred to as that of " Galilee man ".

The " Lady of Lloyds " skull was found, as has been indicated, in the heart of London. It came to light when workmen were engaged digging out the site for the new Royal Exchange which the Corporation of Lloyds have had erected in Leadenhall Street.

Deep down below the streets of London are ancient land surfaces which were laid out during the Glacial and Post-glacial epochs. The River Thames has not always flowed at its present level. In early Pleistocene times it was much higher, for the valley had not been scooped out. At a much later period the valley, which the river had shaped, was so deep that the bed of the Thames was far below the present street level. The river was then often a fiercely roaring torrent which carried down great quantities of mud and gravel, and it frequently overflowed its banks, flooding a considerable part of the valley. The mud and gravel were accumulated in such thick masses that the river bed was gradually raised, and the Thames ultimately became somewhat placid in its flow. Bones of animals which had perished in the valley were occasionally swept down by floods and embedded in the masses of mud and stone that now lie in compact masses below the buildings of modern London.

During the Ice Age the ancient river banks were covered with Arctic mosses and dwarf willows and birches. Animals which have long been extinct were then prowling about. These included the monstrous hairy mammoth beside which a modern elephant would seem a pigmy, the fierce woolly rhinoceros with two sharp tusks protruding from its snout, the reindeer that scraped the snow in winter to find the mosses on which it fed, the big wild ox, &c. There were also human beings of an extinct type. Neanderthal men who made flint tools of Mousterian type hunted wild animals in the Thames valley, and, when the climate grew particularly severe, they

SCENE OF THE DISCOVERY OF THE GALILEE SKULL

The interior of the Robbers' Cave near Tabgha, north of Tiberias

By courtesy of the British School of Archæology in Jerusalem and Mr. F. Turville-Petre

may have sought shelter in caves which have long been buried out of sight.

The excavation on the site of Lloyds' building were carried down to a depth of more than forty feet. In the " blue clay " below gravel was found the limb bone of the woolly rhinoceros. A number of animal remains were taken from the gravel, including part of a thigh bone and some molar teeth of the great hairy mammoth, the antlers and some limb bones of the red deer, and the skull of a wild ox.

Mr. Warren R. Dawson, the zoologist, was deeply interested in these finds and exhibited them at a meeting of the Zoological Society.

On visiting the site one day his attention was attracted by the most interesting discovery of all—some fragments of bone which had been found at a depth of about forty-two feet below the present street-level. These fragments had lain for thousands of years in a bed of river gravel of the lowest level in the Thames valley.

Mr. Dawson recognized that the fragments were those of a human skull, and noted that their mineralized condition indicated great antiquity. Having obtained permission to submit them to an expert anatomist and anthropologist, he carried them to Professor G. Elliot Smith of University College, London, and that scientist was able to show that the fragments had formed two-thirds of the skull of a left-handed woman between forty-five and fifty years of age.

The skull shows points of resemblance to one of the Neanderthal race. Unfortunately the forehead is missing, and it is unknown whether the eyebrow ridges were similar to those of the Neanderthals. It is not certain whether the skull is that of a Neanderthal of a later period than the

Continental Neanderthals, or of an intermediate type. If the skull is of the modern species, it is nearer the Neanderthal type than any other previously found.

With the exception of the Piltdown skull, that of the "Lady of Lloyds" is the oldest human skull yet found in Britain. Like the bones of the extinct animals from the site of Lloyds' building, the skull fragments were probably washed down by an ancient Thames flood from higher ground—perhaps from a cave in which ancient hunters had dwelt.

No other bones of this ancient woman were found, but Professor Elliot Smith was able to state that she had been left-handed. The skull of a right-handed person shows a particular development on the left side and that of a left-handed person on the right side of the skull. In the "Lady of Lloyds" skull the features of left-handedness are well marked.

The Galilee skull is now preserved in Jerusalem and that of the "Lady of Lloyds" in University College, London.

In 1925 a battered skull of Neanderthal type was found in a quarry near Weimar in Germany. It lay embedded among fragments of charred wood and bone, and some are of opinion it should therefore be regarded as evidence that some of the Neanderthal peoples were cannibals.

CHAPTER VIII

World-wide Traces of Early Hunters

It is in Europe that most of our information regarding the habits, customs, and industries of Neanderthal man have, so far, been obtained, the reason being that our continent has been more thoroughly explored than the other continents.

Neanderthal man appears to have wandered and hunted from end to end of Europe. His tools and weapons of Mousterian type have been found in old river gravels, in rock shelters and in caves in Spain, in France, on the island of Jersey in the English Channel, in England (but not in Scotland and Ireland), in Italy, in Belgium, in Germany, in Austria, in Poland, and in southern Russia. By studying these relics closely, and taking note of the layers in which they have been discovered, it has been possible to arrange them into three periods which are referred to as Early, Middle, and Late Mousterian.

Our knowledge of the physical characters of the Neanderthal hunters is derived not only from skulls but from whole skeletons.

At Ferrassie, in the Dordogne valley, France, two skeletons of adults in a good state of preservation and two of children almost destroyed were brought to light between 1909 and 1911. One of the adults was a man, and as certain of his bones were missing, it has been suggested that the ancient hunter may have been killed and partly devoured by a beast of prey. The other adult was a woman, and her arms had been folded and laid upon her breast before she was buried in a crouched position.

The most complete skeleton of a Neanderthal man which has yet been discovered, lay in a small cave with a low roof at La Bouffia Bonneval, near La Chapelle-aux-Saints, Corrèze, in France. It was brought to light in 1908. The body was in a sleeping posture with the right arm stretched out, and beside it had been laid the horn and some large bones of a bison. The earth above the skeleton contained a number of tools of the " middle " Mousterian period, and many of them had been broken as if on purpose. The custom of breaking the tools and weapons of a dead man is known to have been practised by several peoples in modern times, and a similar custom may, for all we know, have been observed by some of the Neanderthals. There were layers of cinders in the cave, showing that fires had been lit there, and there were bones of the woolly rhinoceros, the reindeer, the bison, the marmot, the horse, the wolf, &c. As the small cave is one which could not have been very suitable to live in, it has been suggested that the animal bones, as well as the tools, were offerings to the dead, and that flesh had been cooked on fires at different times in the belief that the dead man would partake of it. The custom of placing food in a grave was common in later times.

Although, however, Europe has yielded so much information about Neanderthal man, it is certain that he had his original home in some other part of the world. When he entered Europe his method of making stone tools had been well developed; he knew how to produce and use fire, and he had acquired great skill and experience as a tracker and hunter of wild animals.

The discovery of the Galilee skull proves, as has been indicated, that Neanderthal man was living in western Asia. It is known, too, that he was in Africa. In 1921 a Neanderthal skull was found in a cave at Broken Hill, in Rhodesia, which is situated about 650 miles north of Bulawayo. This relic is now known as the skull of " Rhodesian man ".

The cave from which the skull was taken has been called the " Bone Cave ", because it contains an immense quantity of animal remains in a fossilized or partly fossilized condition. Among the animals represented in the finds are those of the hippopotamus, the rhinoceros, the elephant, the lion, the leopard, the antelope, &c., as well as numerous birds.

The skull of "Rhodesian man" is almost complete and has prominent eyebrow ridges and a retreating forehead. In outward appearance the African Neanderthal must have closely resembled the Neanderthals of Europe. Scientists have found, however, that the ancient Rhodesian had a more highly developed brain than is indicated by any Neanderthal skull yet discovered in our continent, and it is possible he was a more advanced and later type than the European representatives of the ancient race.

Near his skull were found some remains of another individual, or individuals, including a fragment of an upper jaw, a complete leg bone, parts of an arm bone, and some smaller bones.

No skulls or bones of members of the Neanderthal races have been discovered elsewhere in Africa, but Mousterian tools, which had been made and used by groups of Neanderthal hunters, have been collected in Egypt, on the Sahara Desert, and along the north African coast, chiefly in Algeria and Morocco.

It is possible that some of the Neanderthals entered Europe from Africa across a Mediterranean land-bridge. Italy was, during the period of their wanderings and at a later period, connected with Africa and also with Malta. The ancient hunters may have gone northward by way of Italy. Some think that those who reached the country now known as Morocco walked across a land-bridge at Gibraltar.

It was at Gibraltar that the first known Neanderthal skull

was found in 1848, the discoverer being Lieut. Flint of the Royal Artillery. It was placed in a local museum, but did not attract much attention until after another of similar type was found in 1857 in the limestone cave of Neanderthal (near Düsseldorf in Germany), which has given the modern name to the ancient race.

If there was a land-bridge at Gibraltar during the Third Inter-glacial and Early Fourth Glacial epochs, it must have been a restored one. The strait of Gibraltar was open at the close of the Pliocene Age, and the Balearic Isles, then forming one large group or two groups, had been separated from Spain.

The evidence that the strait of Gibraltar was open is provided by two types of marine molluscs which are still common in the cold waters of northern Europe. When the Ice Age came on, these molluscs spread southward to the Spanish coasts and then entered the Mediterranean at Gibraltar and reached as far eastward as Sicily and the southern coast of Italy, where they are now found completely fossilized. There must, therefore, have been a clear way for them from the Atlantic to the western part of the Mediterranean during a very cold period. Had there been a land-bridge at Gibraltar, these molluscs could never have reached the Italian coast.

The evidence that the Balearic Isles were separated from Spain from the close of the Pliocene Age is provided by the finds of the bones of animals which had been developed in isolation from the rest of Europe for thousands of years. One was about the size of a fox, with short stumpy legs, and it had horns. It fed upon plants and climbed the rocks. This peculiar animal is unknown elsewhere in Europe, except, perhaps, in Sardinia, where the remains of an animal of somewhat similar type have been discovered. There were gigantic tortoises on the Balearic group and these had undoubtedly survived from the Pliocene Age. The land-bridge that connected the island group with Spain must, therefore, have been broken before the Ice Age came on. If the land had risen during an Inter-glacial epoch and restored the land-bridge at Gibraltar, the Balearic island group should have been connected once again with Spain, but, apparently, this did not happen.

It seems highly probable that the Neanderthal hunters who reached Gibraltar did not cross over from Morocco but came southward through Spain.

While groups of Neanderthal hunters may have entered Europe across the Italian land-bridge from Africa, others may have entered it from Asia. As has been noted, Mousterian tools and weapons have been found in southern Russia. Some were in the " Wolf Cave " in the Crimea and others at a site in the province of Kuban in the Caucasus. Similar finds have been made in Asia Minor. Palestine, as we have seen, had its Neanderthal hunters. Near Eriwan in Transcaucasia some interesting Mousterian relics have come to light. For a good many years it has been known that hand-axes of quartzite of the Chellean and Acheulian types have been unearthed in India, but it is not known what species of humanity made and used them, for no skulls or skeletons have yet been found. Similar finds in Ceylon, Indo-China, and Japan may be noted.

Of late interesting discoveries of relics of the ancient hunters have been made in Central Asia and northern China. American archæologists who visited the Gobi Desert in 1925 collected quantities of ancient flints, among which were certain pointed flakes and chipped side-scrapers said to be very similar to those of the Mousterian industry in Europe. Others, however, were of later type.

More definite evidence was obtained by French archæologists who in 1923 found, at different places in the provinces of Ordos and Shensi, in northern China, Mousterian tools and fossilized animal bones. These relics were deeply buried under the yellow loess formations that were deposited during the last phase of the Ice Age.

Loess, it should be explained, is a fine sandy loam which was produced by the constant grinding of rocks by great masses of moving ice during the Glacial epochs. When the ice melted the loess was in places heaped up by the action of water and fresh-water shells are found in it. The greatest quantities were, however, blown through the air by strong winds and heaped against ridges of rock and along river banks. In Central Asia at the present day dust-storms are common, not only during the dry winter season but also in summer. This drifting of the sandy loam, which is still going on, has been in progress for many thousands of years, with the result that in some areas immense deposits of loess are to be found.

During the Second Inter-glacial, the Third Inter-glacial, and the Post-glacial epochs the loess left by the vanished glaciers was lifted and carried by winds to be distributed over vast areas in Europe and Asia. The broad river valleys of western and central Europe and south-eastern Russia have heavy deposits of wind-blown loess. In some places it lies in deep level beds; in others it bulks in the lee of mountain ranges like heavy snow-drifts.

The " yellow earth " of China and Mongolia is loess, and above it lies the black earth of later formation in which vegetation has long been flourishing. When rivers changed their beds owing to various causes, and cut through the loess, new valleys were formed, and some of these valleys are to-day flanked by steep cliffs of packed and hardened loess.

The French archæologists who were in 1923 exploring in northern China one day entered a ravine which had been cut out of loess, and saw at a depth of fifty feet in a loess cliff a layer of Palæolithic tools and a fire-hearth similar to the Mousterian hearths of western Europe. The tools were of quartzite and some were of Mousterian type, while among the animal bones were those of the woolly rhinoceros, the hyæna, the wild ox, the wild ass, the ostrich, &c.

At another site, about 150 miles farther east, the Frenchmen, while exploring a deep ravine, found in a loess cliff, about 180 feet below the level of the plain, some very small worked flints and the broken and fossilized bones of animals. There were complete skulls of the woolly rhinoceros and the bones of elephants, wild asses, gazelles, giant deer, cave-hyænas, &c. Parts of the antlers of deer, which were taken out of the same layer, seemed to have been used as tools or tool handles.

Fragments of ostrich eggs were also found. As some of the tools were older than others, it was believed that the relics of different periods had been mixed up in the loess, after having been tossed about by strong winds.

The third site was in an area in Shensi where the loess was in places about 500 feet in depth. In gravel below the loess were found some quartzite flakes which were of human workmanship. Evidently an ancient race of mankind lived in the country we now know as China before the yellow loess had been deposited.

In Europe, as in eastern Asia, the worked tools of human

beings have been found buried in loess along with the bones of extinct animals. These tools can, however, be classified, because similar tools lie undisturbed in their layers in the caves. Those found in China cannot, on the other hand, be similarly arranged in chronological order, because no cave evidence has yet been forthcoming to indicate the sequence of the various specimens.

America has yielded traces of early man. At Trenton in New Jersey, U.S.A., hand-axes and Mousterian tools have been detected in gravel of the Pleistocene Age in association with the remains of the hairy mammoth, the musk ox, the reindeer, and the mastodon type of elephant. Similar tools have been discovered in Indiana and Ohio.

In Florida further finds of like character were made in 1925. Mr. Harold J. Cook has announced that in undisturbed Pleistocene sand and gravel he found, at a depth of over five feet, three worked flints which lay beneath the fossilized bones of an extinct type of bison. "It is possible," he wrote (in *Science*, 20th Nov., 1925), "that the bison had been shot and carried these flint-points with him to the place where he finally died and was entombed." This find recalls an earlier one in Logan County, Kansas, where an arrow-head was found under a bone of an extinct species of bison.

In Florida, Professor Loomis recently discovered articles made by human beings lying below the bones of mammoths and mastodons.

Hand-axes and elephant bones have been taken from gravels in northern Mexico, and hand-axes, not, however, in association with bones of animals or human beings, were discovered some years ago in Brazil, Patagonia, and the Argentine, South America.

A number of ancient human skulls and bones, and some fairly complete skeletons, have been unearthed in North America from time to time, but it has not been proved that any of these are of the Pleistocene Age. Human remains found embedded in loess in the Argentine have been much discussed, and their age is uncertain.

Some hold that the fossil remains of South America and Lower California are those of a race different to the Red Indians of the present day. There are, however, several types of American Indians. No bones of Neanderthal man have yet been found in the Americas, and we must, therefore, leave the question of his presence in that part of the world an open one.

CHAPTER IX

Stories told by Cave Deposits

The cave-dwellers of Mousterian times were of very untidy habits. They never had "spring cleanings": indeed, they seem not to have done any sweeping at all. They left all sorts of rubbish lying about. When they ate their food, they cast the bones aside, and these became covered over with the dust which was often blown into the cave. If they chipped flint or quartzite or other stones to make tools or weapons, the fragments were left where they had fallen. When a fire was lit the charcoal of the last fire was thrust by hand or with a piece of wood to one side and became mixed up with other debris which was trampled under foot by the cave-men and women and children. In the course of time a great deal of rubbish accumulated in this way in a cave and the floor-level consequently rose higher and higher, and became harder and harder. The deposits of the various families who lived in a cave from time to time have thus been preserved till our own day, and the scientists who dig through the deposits are able to tell us a great deal about the habits of the ancient untidy people. Sometimes they come across the skeletons of individuals who had died in a cave and were left lying under a heap of rubbish. In some cases shallow graves had been dug, and the mourners placed on the body some objects which were supposed to be required by their lost friend.

In some cases it has been found that after caves were deserted by hunters, wild animals used them as lairs. Cave-lions carried to the caves portions of the animals they had caught and devoured them there. When human beings again took possession of the cave, their own rubbish covered over the relics of the beasts of prey.

In most of the caves in which the Neanderthal hunters lived the bones found are chiefly those of the shoulders and flanks of animals killed in the chase. Ribs and portions of backbones are very rare. It would appear therefore that when the Neanderthals hunted in the open they did not carry or haul to their caves whole carcasses of animals, but that they took cuts from them. It is evident from the finds that a preference was shown for the long bones containing marrow.

It is probable that the ancient hunters often found it very necessary to make haste in cutting up the bodies of animals. Beasts of prey were numerous and would speedily scent a "kill". Neanderthal man was slow-footed, and he would be better able to get away in safety, carrying cuts of flesh, if he left behind him a large part of an animal for the bears, lions, and hyænas. He might prove himself a match for a big bear in a dark cave, but it was a more difficult task to fight a bear in the open.

As the climate of Europe grew colder during the Fourth Glacial epoch, the Neanderthal families gradually moved southward. They were attracted to the Riviera, among other places, for there, sheltered from the north winds by a mountain range, the strip of Mediterranean coast-land was favoured with sunnier and milder weather than most of the districts farther north.

Near Mentone, on the borders of modern France and Italy, Neanderthal man found suitable caves. No fewer than nine of them pierce a great limestone cliff, and the largest has an entrance about twenty-three feet wide and it expands inside, rising to a height of about sixty-five feet.

For many long centuries the winds have been blowing great quantities of sand and dust into these caves, and from time to time there have been falls of rock from the roofs. In some of the caves the soil accumulated to a depth of about thirty feet.

The people living in Mentone and its neighbourhood used to take from these caves large quantities of the fine wind-sifted earth to lay in their gardens, and they often found ancient flint tools and the bones of animals. No attempt at systematic research was made, however, until 1870, when a French scientist began digging for relics in one of the caves. He was deeply interested to find the bones of a number of extinct animals, including those of the woolly rhinoceros, the wild ox, the cave-lion, the cave-bear, the cave-hyæna, &c. In other caves human skeletons were brought to light, and it then became apparent that at Mentone a great deal of information regarding ancient times could be obtained.

The Prince of Monaco was so deeply interested in the early finds that he purchased two of the caves so that their contents might be carefully examined by skilled archæologists. Workers were then employed to clear out the soil, each layer being marked off carefully and its relics noted, so that the evidence of the different periods might be recorded in proper order.

In the upper layers of soil in the Prince's caves were found the bones of birds, &c., which are still to be seen in the Mentone district. Below these the scientists came across evidence of a cooler climate, the remains of animals being those of the types that nowadays live high up in the Alps and in the northern parts of Europe. When these animals lived at Mentone, the winters must have been very severe.

Farther down in the cave-soil lay the bones of extinct animals. Much interest was taken in the discovery of the skull of a huge cave-bear. When that animal hibernated in the Mentone caves the climate on the Riviera in the winter season must have been similar to that of northern Siberia at the present time. The summers were sunny but rather short.

One of the Mentone caves has been named *Grotte des Enfants* (cave of infants), because the skeletons of two very young children were taken from a layer of the soil, which yielded also the remains of Alpine plants and animals.

In the next layer the scientists found the skeleton of a woman. It was associated with the relics of a period when cold-loving animals roamed through pine forests in the neighbourhood of the caves.

Lower down in the soil were the bones of such animals as the woodland reindeer and the wild boar, and still lower down were the smoke-blackened hearths of hunters who had lived for a period in the cave, and used flints of a type which has been called Aurignacian, after the town of Aurignac, near the Pyrenees, in France, where similar ancient tools have been found.

The layer below the hearth contained relics which showed that the climate was less severe than some of the upper layers gave evidence of. Among the animal bones were those of the wild horse, the ibex, the wolf, the fox, and the cave-lion. The beasts of prey had carried into the cave parts of their "kills" and devoured them there. A heap of stones resembling a cairn was found in the same layer. Evidently human beings had lived for a time in the cave, having cleared it of beasts of prey.

Below the cairn were remains of animals that lived among fir trees. The Mentone climate must then have been similar to that of Alaska in our own time.

Digging farther down, the explorers next found a layer which was composed chiefly of pieces of rock that had fallen from the roof of the cave. There were no traces of human beings or animals.

When these rocks were cleared out, it was found that before the cave roof began to crumble, the Mentone climate had been mild enough for such animals as the rabbit, the roe-deer, the fallow-deer, the stag, the ibex, wild cattle, and for the leopard and the fox. Smoke-blackened stones indicated that hunters sometimes lived in the cave during this period.

In the next layer was found the skeleton of a very tall man of the type now known as Cro-Magnon, which will be dealt with in the next chapter.

Below the grave of that hunter were the skeletons of a

woman and a lad with protruding jaws, and near them were flints and the bones of the wild horse, the ibex, and the hyæna.

Under these skeletons were traces of fires which had been lit by hunters, and lower down were flint tools of the Mousterian type which had been left behind by members of the Neanderthal race. These Mousterian relics lay above gravel which had been washed in by the sea. Below the gravel were the bones of cave-hyænas, the earliest-known inhabitants of the natural shelter.

The cave thus unfolded a very remarkable story of remote times. Neanderthal hunters had dwelt in it for a period and then vanished. Wild animals of an extinct type afterwards took possession of the cave, but were ejected by human beings who lit fires. These were hunters, but they were of a different race from the Neanderthals. They had bodies and heads like those of modern Europeans, but their jaws were not of European type.

After a time a taller and more vigorous race of human beings occupied the cave. They had long heads and short broad faces. When they arrived, the Fourth Glacial stage had already reached its height and was in process of passing away very slowly and very gradually.

In the next chapter we shall obtain glimpses of the period of transition during which the Neanderthal cave-dwellers disappeared and the new cave-dwellers became fairly numerous.

MAGDALENIAN PAINTINGS OF BISON AND DEER, FROM THE CAVE OF ALTAMIRA, NEAR SANTANDER, SPAIN

From copies of the originals by L'Abbé Breuil. See page 69

CHAPTER X

The Ancestors of Modern Man

When the Fourth Glacial stage was beginning to decline, there were in western Europe short warm summers but severe and long winters. Oak and chestnut trees were growing in sheltered valleys, but on the hill-sides were firs only. In some parts the country, as indicated, resembled Alaska and northern Siberia at the present time.

Reindeer and woolly mammoths were common in France, and there were large herds of wild horses and bison. Big stags were often seen in the summer season. Cave-lions, cave-bears, and woolly rhinoceri had grown somewhat rare.

Although the advance of the ice-sheet had been arrested and the glaciers were shrinking slowly, many centuries had to pass before the greater part of Europe could become suitable for mankind. Snow and ice lay on the mountains all summer, and the nights were cold. During the winter there were terrific storms.

Slow-footed Neanderthal man suffered greatly during the long Fourth Glacial period. When the climate began to change, and the animals he hunted migrated northward during summer, he was forced to follow them.

Probably the Neanderthal hunter often perished, like the animals he followed, far from his cave shelters. His numbers certainly declined and ultimately Neanderthal man vanished completely from western Europe.

New races were beginning to appear in southern and western Europe. These differed very much from the low-browed, slow-footed Neanderthals and were of the species known as " Modern Man " (*Homo sapiens.*) They had high foreheads, long nimble legs, and erect bodies. Judging from their skeletons, it is evident that they could run fast—fast enough, indeed, to keep up with the animals they hunted. There are still Indians in Mexico who are so swift-footed and long-winded that they can follow the chase until the deer become exhausted. The skeletons of the early representatives of Modern Man have broad and deep chests, as well as the long shin bones of fast runners. Evidently they were fine athletes.

The earliest European types of Modern Man of the early Post-glacial stage are represented by two skeletons which have been found in the *Grotte des Enfants* near Mentone. Dr. Elliot Smith, who recently examined these skeletons, states that one is that of a woman about thirty years and the other of a boy of thirteen. He thinks that they resembled somewhat the modern Australian savages. It is customary to refer to the two skeletons as those of representatives of the " Grimaldi race ".

A higher type of mankind arrived later. It is represented by a number of skeletons and is referred to nowadays as the " Cro-Magnon race ". The Cro-Magnons were so like the people of modern Europe that if groups of them were to be restored to life to-day and were attired in modern clothing, they might walk through our streets without attracting special attention. We might, however, be struck by the fine physical development of some of the men and especially the tall Cro-Magnons. If they were to take part in the Olympic games, they would be among the record-breakers, especially in the Marathon race.

The Cro-Magnons were of two types, tall and short, but all had certain features in common. Their heads were large and long—larger than the average European head of to-day. Their foreheads were high, their noses narrow, and their chins well developed. Compared with the length of their skulls, their faces were short and they had high and broad cheek bones.

One male Cro-Magnon skeleton found in a cave near Mentone measured 6 feet 4½ inches, and other skeletons found in south-western France were those of men who were slightly under or slightly over 6 feet in height. The women were not so tall as the men, their stature varying from 5 feet 5 inches to 5 feet 7 inches.

The shorter Cro-Magnon type includes the small man, 5 feet 3 inches in height, represented by a skeleton found in a shelter at Combe-Capelle in the Dordogne valley in France. Some think that Combe-Capelle man resembled the Galley Hill man of an earlier period. It may be that the Cro-Magnons were related to the earlier hunters who were living in western Europe before the low-browed Neanderthals entered it.

We do not know for certain whether or not the Cro-Magnons came into touch with the low-browed, slow-footed Neanderthals. The languages of the two races would be quite different.

Some have suggested that the Cro-Magnons probably exterminated the Neanderthals in warfare. It is more likely that the latter died out, owing to the changing conditions of life. Possibly the last remaining groups of them perished of diseases brought into Europe by the Cro-Magnons, just as the natives of Tasmania, after white men settled on their island, died very quickly, being unable to resist diseases brought from

Europe. Similarly, after the Spaniards entered South America, many thousands of natives in the Amazon valley died from measles, which raged like a plague, because it was a new disease in that area and the natives did not know how to treat it, and did not have in their blood the substance which resists the germs of measles.

Although the new race has been called Cro-Magnons, after the French village of that name, where skeletons have been found, the first Cro-Magnon skeleton was discovered in 1823 in " Goat's Hole ", the name of a cave at Paviland near Rhossilly, Gower Peninsula, South Wales. This cave is situated on the face of a sandstone cliff over 30 feet above the present sea-level; it is about 60 feet long, 200 feet broad, and over 25 feet high.

At the time when the Paviland cave was occupied by the Cro-Magnon hunters it was on shore-level. A skeleton has been found in the cave of a Cro-Magnon who must have been buried when the climate of South Wales was so severe that the great hairy mammoth was living in the valleys. The tusks and skull of a mammoth were found in the cave near the human skeleton, which was that of a tall man.

All the bones of this Paviland skeleton were found to be red, the body, before burial, having been smeared with red earth. This was an ancient custom. The people who practised it probably believed that one was made stronger and more vigorous by having the skin painted red, the colour of blood.

It appears that the ancient people who smeared a dead man with a red mixture, believed that he would be revived by it in time and would awake and come forth from the cave.

The bodies of the Cro-Magnon dead were usually laid with

their faces towards the cave entrance. Amulets, which were supposed to give power to the dead, were also placed on different parts of the body. The Paviland man had a waist-belt of shells and a long necklace of little rods of ivory. Ivory rings, a small bone from the forepaw of a wolf, as well as an object shaped like a tongue, were also found beside the skeleton.

Five skeletons of the same race as the "Red Man of Paviland" (as he is called) were found in 1868 in a cave at the village of Cro-Magnon, near Les Eyzies in France. One skeleton was that of an old man; it is now referred to as the "Old Man of Cro-Magnon". Two skeletons were those of young men. Near them were fragments of a child's skeleton and the skeleton of a woman whose forehead had been injured by a heavy blow. The woman had a very large brain. In fact, it was larger than is the average male brain in Europe in our own day.

All the Cro-Magnons whose skulls have been found had large brains. As a scientist has said: "They required large brains because they had to discover much and invent much, being the pioneers of modern civilization."

When the Cro-Magnons entered the hunting-fields of western Europe they had to live strenuous lives. If animals on which they fed were numerous, so were the beasts of prey. They had better implements than were possessed by the Neanderthals, and these implements have been called "Aurignacian". Aurignacian tools include hand-knives (sharp on one side and blunt on the other so as to be grasped comfortably), scrapers, and finely-worked borers, hammer-stones, planing-tools, points, and gravers which were used by artists. They had also bone lance-heads and throwing-stones. Some of the small flint tools with edges and points would have been useful in fishing.

The Aurignacian industry appears to have been introduced into western Europe across the Italian land-bridge from

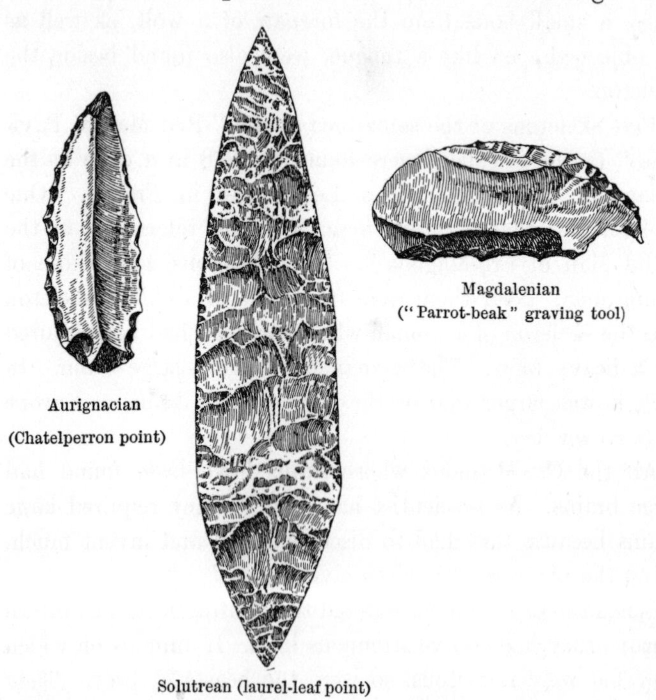

Aurignacian (Chatelperron point)

Magdalenian ("Parrot-beak" graving tool)

Solutrean (laurel-leaf point)

Upper Palæolithic Implements

North Africa. It spread, on the one hand, over modern France and into the north of modern Spain, and, on the other, into modern Austria and the western parts of modern Germany. In modern England, Aurignacian tools were, until recently, found chiefly in the south-west. The cave known as Kent's

Hole near Torquay has yielded Aurignacian relics, as has also the Goat's Hole cave at Paviland already referred to. Of late, however, some Aurignacian tools have been discovered in the "Pinhole cave" at Cresswell Crags, Derbyshire.

The Cro-Magnons who hunted in England were not likely to have spread into the cold and barren tracts of the north. There were still glaciers in Cumberland and Scotland, and the severe winters would cause the animals of the chase to move towards the south. It is not likely that many of the Cro-Magnons lived in the country we know as England until the climate improved greatly. The early hunters of this race may have come only on hunting expeditions during the short summers.

CHAPTER XI

Cave Pictures of Ancient Times

Wonderful records of the life and times of Cro-Magnon man are to be found in great caves and rock shelters in France and Spain.

The ancient artists and sculptors made vivid studies of wild animals, and in some cases of the men who hunted them. They also depicted beasts of prey, fishes, and plants. Certain articles of horn, bone, and ivory, which were used in ceremonies or carried by men of rank, were decorated with forms of animals and with mysterious symbols.

The discovery that the Cro-Magnon people had a wonderful art was first made about half a century ago by a Spanish nobleman and his daughter, a child of five. It chanced that a fox had during a hunt taken refuge in a hole at Altamira near Santillana del Mar, in the north of Spain. Men set to work to dig it out and in doing so they discovered a cave. At the mouth of this cave lay some of the tools of the ancient hunters of prehistoric times.

The nobleman, the Marquis of Sautuola, afterwards entered the Altamira cave to search for prehistoric relics. While he was engaged in digging, his little girl lit a candle and walked into the depths of the cave. She had not gone far when she saw pictures on the roof and she called out: "Bulls! bulls!" Her father left his work and went to find what had attracted her attention, and he was greatly astonished to see a number of ancient paintings and engravings of animals.

At the time few believed that these pictures were very ancient, but after some years had gone past, other discoveries of like character were made which aroused keen interest among scholars.

It chanced that the cave of La Mouthe in the Dordogne valley in south-western France was being cleared of the rubbish which had accumulated for thousands of years. In this rubbish were found relics of the Cro-Magnon hunters. During the digging operations an inner cave was discovered, and on its walls were paintings of animals. These paintings were evidently older than the relics found in the rubbish which blocked the entrance.

Other caves with paintings were subsequently cleared. In one case the figures of the animals were partly covered with stalactite which had taken many hundreds of years to form.

The surest proof of the great age of the pictures, however, is found in their subjects. Among the animals which had been depicted by the ancient hunters were the reindeer, the hairy mammoth, and the woolly rhinoceros. The artist who drew and painted these animals must have been living when

The Deer Drive—a mural painting in dark red in the Cueva de los Caballos near Abucácer, Castellón, Spain

northern Europe was covered with ice, and the countries we now know as France and Spain had cold climates in winter.

Most of the caves in which the animal pictures have been found are very deep and dark. Those who nowadays enter them have to make their way with care by the light of candles or electric flash-lights. Some paintings are found at a distance of over half a mile from the entrance. In a narrow fissure of one cave there is a painting of a rhinoceros, which can only be seen by the aid of a mirror. Of late certain caves with ancient paintings have been fitted with electric lamps so that tourists may explore them and see the work of the ancient artists.

When the ancient artists themselves crept into the depths of the long, twisting caves they used lamps. Some of these lamps have been discovered. They are little shallow bowls with flat handles, which had been cut out of sandstone by workers who used small flint tools. On the bottom of one is a lovely engraving of the head and horns of an ibex.

The shallow basin of the ancient stone lamps was filled with animal fat in which was stuck a wick of dried moss. When the wick was lit, the flame was fed by the melting grease. Lamps of similar type are still used by peasants in the Dordogne valley in France, and they are not unlike the Highland cruses and the stone lamps used by the Eskimo peoples of the present day. It makes one wonder greatly to think that the lamps invented by Cro-Magnon man should have continued in use for many thousands of years.

The Cro-Magnon artists used bone palettes on which they mixed their colours, and specimens of these have been found; some were carved in animal shape. Probably the artists' brushes were made of hair, but not one has survived.

Colours were prepared by grinding small nodules of iron and manganese ores which give shades of red and yellow and blue-black. Burned bones gave black pigment and Kaolin clay white pigment. The dry pigments were enclosed by the Cro-Magnons in hollow bones and were mixed with grease on the palettes.

When an artist entered the dark and deep inner recess of a cave to make a picture, he probably carried with him a sketch of the animal he meant to depict. Such a sketch could be made on a piece of slate, stone, or bone with charcoal or with a sharp flint. No doubt the artist had an assistant who attended to the lamp or lamps required to provide the necessary light. When the work was finished and the artist returned, the picture could not be seen except by those who crept into the dark and difficult " picture gallery ", using lamps to light up the passages.

It seems clear, therefore, that the cave pictures were not meant to be freely seen and admired by all and sundry. Probably they were supposed to exercise a magical influence. By drawing the picture of an animal in a dark mysterious cave, the Cro-Magnons may have believed that they cast a spell over it, so that they might be able to slay it.

This curious belief is still to be met with among some superstitious peoples. French peasants who want to catch foxes make models of foxes in clay. In the Highlands clay and wax models of animals and men were made so that a magic spell might be cast over them. Some savage peoples make drawings of animals, believing that by so doing they themselves may find and kill a sufficient number of them for food.

When the writer was a boy he used to go bird-nesting with other boys. Those who wanted to collect specimens of wild-birds' eggs were in the habit of performing a curious ceremony.

Before they began to search for nests, they drew on a sandy bank the forms of as many eggs as they wanted to get, each boy repeating as he did so, " I want this and this and this." Apparently the boys were performing a magical ceremony which had come down from long past generations. They believed that they would be sure to find eggs after making drawings of them. There are still in the Highlands wells,

A Line of Animal Tracks which two Hunters are following

Painted in dark red. From Morella la Vella, Castellón, Spain. ¼ actual size

mounds, &c., at which, according to traditional belief, wishes are granted. The individual who " wishes a wish " at a " wishing well ", a " wishing mound ", or a " wishing gate " does so with closed eyes and in silence, and the wish is not revealed to anyone. Perhaps the deep caves were to Cro-Magnon man " wishing caves ".

In some caves it is found that several animals have been drawn or painted on the same spot, one above the other. These different pictures were made at different periods. In one cave, for instance, an early artist drew a hairy mammoth in outline. Then another artist came later and drew a bison

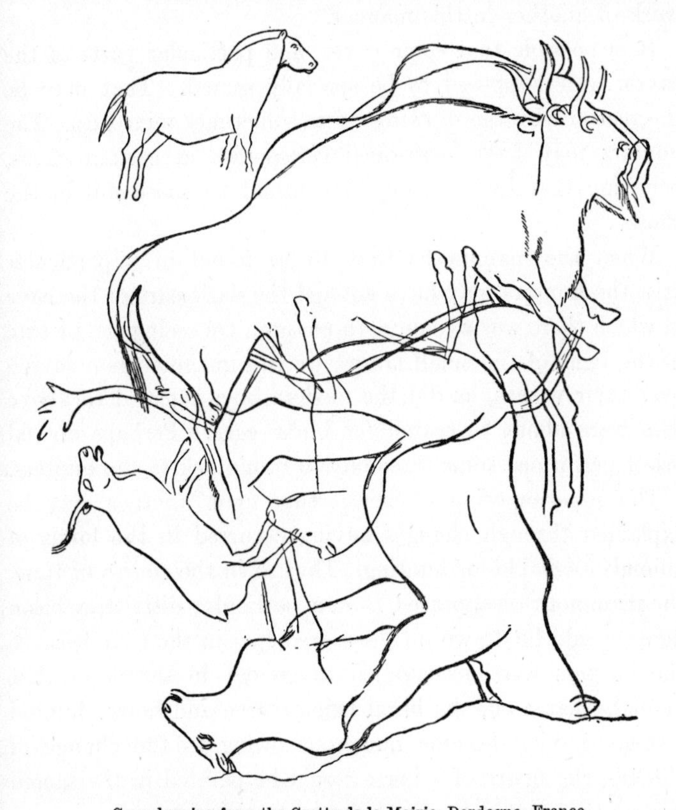

Cave-drawing from the Grotte de la Mairie, Dordogne, France

Bison, Horses, Reindeer, and Bears, drawn at different periods one above the other. (After Breuil.)

over part of the mammoth's figure. Some generations went past, and then an artist selected the same spot for his work and painted the figure of a wild horse over parts of the mammoth and bison. If the figures had been drawn simply to ornament a cave, one artist would not have spoiled the work of another in this manner.

It is possible that some caves, and particular parts of the caves, were supposed to be specially sacred. That may be the reason why the drawings were sometimes mixed up. The hunters may have performed ceremonies in certain caves, believing that by so doing they would be successful in the chase.

When the mammoths were to be found in a particular area the hunters may have entered the dark part of the cave in which there was a mammoth picture. On seeing the picture in the light of the small lamps, we can imagine them saying over their wishes, as did the modern boys referred to above who were about to search for birds' eggs. Perhaps an old priest performed some ceremony to bring luck to the hunters.

The superimposing of one picture upon another may be explained through changes having occurred in the kinds of animals available for hunting. Thus, if in the course of time, the mammoth disappeared from a particular district, a bison figure would be drawn on the sacred spot in the cave because the hunters were accustomed to go out in search of that animal. Later on, the bison being scarce and horses hunted instead, having become numerous owing to the change of climate, the figure of a horse would be painted in the sacred part of the cave above the figure of the bison.

On the bodies of some animals in the caves arrows and lances were drawn as if to indicate that the hunters hoped to be able to slay the animal by wounding it in a vital part. On a figure of a mammoth in outline a big heart was painted. It looks as if in this case the artist believed his picture would give the hunters power to slay the mammoth by casting a spell over its heart.

An interesting picture from one of the French caves is that of a man wearing the complete skin of a stag with the horns on his head, the ears erect, and the tail dangling behind. He is depicted as if he were prancing about in imitation of a deer. Perhaps this is a picture of a masked sorcerer performing some magical ceremony which was supposed to bring good luck to the hunters.

Rock Painting in red at the Cuevas de la Araña, Bicorp, Spain, representing a Gatherer of Wild Honey. Bees enlarged to indicate numbers. Actual size.

Another picture shows a group of nine women dancing in a ring round a male figure, possibly a priest. The ring games which children still play may be relics of ceremonies that were performed in long ages past. In ancient times the children would naturally imitate the ceremonies which they saw performed by the grown-up people. After Christianity was introduced, Pagan ceremonies ceased, but the children kept playing the old games. The Maypole dance, for instance, was long ago a Pagan religious ceremony, and nowadays it is merely a pretty game which has been kept alive by custom.

In certain of the caves in which the Cro-Magnon people lived, one can still see on the rock the impressions of human hands. Some of the ancient people who made these marks had smeared their hands with red earth mixed with grease before pressing them on the rock. Others laid their hands flat on the walls of the caves and smeared the colouring matter all round them and between the fingers. Perhaps this was another ceremony which was supposed to bring luck to the hands of hunters and workers.

These impressions of Cro-Magnon hands are specially interesting because they indicate that portions of fingers had in some cases been cut off. We do not know for certain whether or not such mutilations were due to accident or were done deliberately. The custom of chopping off the joints of fingers was practised until recently by some tribes of Red Indians in North America, by the dark tribes of Australian natives, and by the Bushman peoples of South Africa. There are references in Scottish Highland folk-stories to the custom. One reason for sacrificing a finger joint has been given by the Red Indians. They explained that when some particular disease broke out in a tribe or family, causing many deaths, the survivors believed they would be spared if they cut off one or more finger joints.

In the inner recesses of one of the French caves the floor is covered with clay, and at one point there is an impression of a human foot. A little hillock of clay has the marks left by human heels, as if a worker had been engaged in mixing the clay. There were also lumps of kneaded clay with finger-marks on them. Near the hillock were found two clay models of bison, each about two feet long, which a Cro-Magnon artist had formed.

To reach this part of the cave the explorers had to break through a " fence " of stalactites. It had evidently not been visited since the Cro-Magnon clay-workers had left it. One or two flakes of flint had been dropped and also a pierced tooth of an ox. A stream deep enough to float a small boat runs out of this cave, and the walls of the cave are covered with engravings of animals.

The inner cave in which the clay models of bison were found is at the end of a narrow passage which was reached by a ladder. Apparently the inner cave was a sacred place which few visited in ancient times. It is wonderful to think that the very footprints of the last Cro-Magnons who entered it can still be seen.

The temperature of the inner cave never varies during the year, and that is why everything in it has been so well preserved.

The vast majority of the caves in which the Cro-Magnon artists worked are situated in southern France and north-western Spain. Engravings have, so far, been found in only one cave in Italy—that of Romanelli near Castro, Terra d'Otranto. In " Bacon's Hole " cave near Swansea, in South Wales, lines of red colour on rock are said to date back till the time of the Cro-Magnon hunters.

CHAPTER XII

Early Settlers in England and Scotland

At the close of the Palæolithic period the climate of Europe was gradually growing milder. The ice-cap in the north retreated farther and farther during the summer seasons and the melting ice caused great floods.

In the course of centuries the land rose as the ice vanished. When there were about 3000 feet of ice on Scotland and Denmark and about 6000 feet of ice over Norway and Sweden, the land had been depressed by the tremendous burden upon it. Then during the melting period the floods caused periodic deluges, forming lakes and marshes. In time, however, a great part of the North Sea land-bridge was restored, as was also the English Channel valley. Once again the Baltic became an inland lake, and men and animals could walk from modern France to modern England.

During the period of Magdalenian civilization (the final period of the Late Palæolithic Age), the climate of England was very cold. The hunters, however, although not numerous, were daring, and during the short summer seasons they followed the reindeer as far north as the area now known as Derbyshire. In the " Pinhole cave " at Cresswell Crags excavators found recently a finely carved lance point of Magdalenian type. It had been shaped from the tusk of a mammoth.

Some of the Cro-Magnon hunters may have crossed the land-bridge that connected the country we know as England with the continent. This land-bridge was, however, severed again during the Magdalenian period. There were, perhaps,

Cro-Magnons in the modern English area who continued in the Aurignacian stage of culture which had been slightly influenced by Solutrean culture.

In the "Pinhole cave" Aurignacian flint and bone tools have been found. The horse, bison, and reindeer were hunted,

Signs and Symbols of late Magdalenian Epoch in Spain

From petroglyphes in Andalusia (after Breuil).

but the reindeer were more numerous than the other wild animals.

The Cro-Magnon hunters who lived in the "Pinhole cave" lit fires. They left behind them a large number of pebbles which had been scorched and cracked by fire, and it is believed that they made use of heated pebbles to cook their food. Small pebbles could be dropped when hot into skin pots containing flesh and water to cook the flesh by boiling and to make soup. Cuts of steak could be roasted between hot stones.

When the Magdalenian period was passing away, the climate in southern and western Europe improved greatly. The summers grew warmer and longer and forests gradually spread far and wide. Plains that had been bleak and barren were covered with vegetation, and the mosses on which reindeer fed disappeared. The reindeer and hairy mammoths gradually retreated towards the north. At the present day the reindeer in the north of Europe seek the hills in summer because in the valleys they are tortured by the insects when the weather grows warm.

As the glaciers melted in the country which we now know as Scotland, the reindeer became more numerous there. Horns of reindeer have been found in large numbers as far north as the Inchnadamph caves in Sutherland.

New races of mankind entered Europe as the climate grew milder. From North Africa a long-headed people of short stature entered Spain and Italy and gradually spread across France; broad-headed peoples also entered Europe from the east, some reaching as far west as modern Spain and Portugal.

These new races brought with them new industries. From North Africa groups of immigrants carried small flints which are called "pigmy flints" or "microliths", some being fish-spear heads and others apparently the "teeth" of wooden harpoons also used for catching fish.

This flint industry was developed in North Africa, as had been the earlier Aurignacian industry which was carried into western Europe by Cro-Magnon man.

In France the pigmy flint industry is called the Tardenoisian, after the finds made at the type station of Fère-en-Tardenois, Aisne, France.

The people who shaped and used these small flints appear to have lived to a great extent on fish and shell-fish. In Portugal their deposits contain quantities of the shells of whelks, oysters, cockles, &c., as well as the bones of wild cattle, deer, sheep, goats, pigs, hares, &c.

The Tardenoisian people have left traces of their activities round the shores of the Mediterranean, from Algiers to Egypt on the south, in Palestine on the east, in Spain and France on the west, and in the British Isles as far north as Scotland. Some Tardenoisian flints have been found in the Crimea and some as far distant as India.

The other industry is known as the Azilian, which has been so named after the typical finds made near the small town of Mas d'Azil at the foot of the Pyrenees. Azilian relics have been unearthed in the north of Spain, in parts of France, in Belgium, and in England and Scotland and in Bavaria. The people who introduced the industry may have come into Europe from the east. They made and used horn harpoons similar to those used in Magdalenian times. The Magdalenian harpoons, however, were made chiefly from reindeer horn, while the Azilian harpoons were always made from red-deer horn. In France the Azilian and Tardenoisian cultures were mixed, and archæologists refer to the late phases of both as Tardenoisian-Azilian.

In the cave of Ofnet in Bavaria, evidence has been found that when the Azilian and Tardenoisian industries were practised in that area, there were mixed groups of long-headed and broad-headed peoples.

Over thirty human skulls were found in the Azilian layer

in the Ofnet cave. When these were examined by experts it was found that they had been cut off the bodies after death. The heads were placed together in the cave facing the west, and the cave opens from the south-west.

Apparently the people of this period believed that the soul was in the head, and that after death it went towards the west, as the sun appears to do each day. Snail-shells and the teeth of stags had been placed on the skulls of women and children, but four men's skulls had none of these amulets on them. The skulls and teeth were apparently supposed to bring luck to the dead as well as to the living.

In Spain and Portugal the Tardenoisian people did not cut off the heads of their dead. Most of the skeletons found in these countries, however, have been those of women and children. It looks, therefore, as if large numbers of the men perished when out hunting. Perhaps many were killed and devoured by beasts of prey.

The art of the Tardenoisian and Azilian peoples differed from that of the Cro-Magnons. On rock shelters and the walls of caves they painted rude figures of animals and curious designs, some of which may have been symbols and some alphabetic characters. They also painted on pebbles designs that must have had some meaning.

A third people entered Europe in the north-eastern area, perhaps from Asia, and spread round the shores of the Baltic while it was yet an inland lake. These are known as the Maglemosians, and some think they were the ancestors of the tall fair northerners (the Nordics). The climate on the Baltic shores had become mild enough to permit of forests growing. The chief tree was the pine, but there were also aspens, hazels, birches, and elms.

Relics of this northern people have been found in the peat moor of Maglemose (Great Moor) near Mullerup on the west coast of Zealand. They appear to have had their homes on rafts on a fresh-water lake at Maglemose, and the relics found in the peat probably dropped from these rafts.

Like the Azilians, the Maglemosians had harpoons, mostly of bone, but chiefly with barbs on one side only. Like the

Azilian. Harpoon from MacArthur Cave, Oban

Tardenoisian ("Pigmy" Flints)

Maglemosian or Azilian-Maglemosian
(Harpoon from rock-shelter, Druimvargie, Oban.)

Tardenoisians they used pigmy flints. The bone needle with the "eye" was in use among the Maglemosians of the Baltic, but no such needle has been found among the Azilian relics of France and Spain.

Drawings of animals in outline and curious designs, which may have been symbols, were engraved on many of the Maglemosian bone and horn tools.

An examination of the animal remains shows that the

Maglemose people hunted the moose, the red-deer, the roe-deer, the wild ox, and the wild pig, and occasionally killed bears and beavers.

Of very special interest is the fact that they had the domesticated dog. No trace of the dog has been found among the Azilian relics. It may be that the Maglemose people were the first settlers in Europe who used the dog to hunt wild animals and warn them of the approach of beasts of prey. It is possible that they had their houses on rafts so as to be safe from these wild animals, especially during the long, dark nights of winter.

Relics of the Azilian period have been found in the MacArthur cave at Oban, which is situated about thirty feet above the present sea-level. It was formerly on the seashore, but it was elevated during the last land movement when Scotland was rising and the south of England was sinking.

During the period when the cave was on the seashore there was still a land-bridge across the English Channel, and another across the North Sea in the area of the Dogger Bank.

In the cave were found tools made of bone and deer horn, twenty flakes or chips of flint, and three " hammer stones ". Among the tools were deer-horn harpoons with barbs on both sides. The flints were, like the harpoons, of Azilian type.

The bones of the domesticated dog were found in the Oban cave. It would therefore seem that the Oban cave-dwellers had been in touch with the Maglemosians, who, as we have seen, had domesticated dogs.

Other relics of the same period were found not far from the cave, and at the base of a steep rock called Druimvargie (pronounced drum-var′a-gee, the " g " being hard). There the harpoons were of bone with barbs on one side only, a form very rare in France. These bone harpoons are of Maglemosian type. Other harpoons were found on the island of Oronsay in the southern Hebrides and on a smaller island near it, and in Kirkcudbright. Two harpoons of Maglemosian type, with barbs on one side, were found under peat near Hull in Yorkshire, one at Hornsea, and one at Skipsea.

It would appear from these finds that the people of Maglemose had come over the North Sea land-bridge into the area now known as Yorkshire. As there were broad rivers and marshes to cross, they may have walked over the ice during the winter season.

A reindeer horn harpoon has been found in the Victoria cave near Settle in Yorkshire, and near it were painted pebbles and other relics of the Azilian people. Perhaps the people who occupied the cave when the reindeer lived in Yorkshire were mixed Azilians and Cro-Magnons of the late Magdalenian period.

Some flints found at Campbeltown in Argyllshire have a Magdalenian appearance, and these may be relics of Cro-Magnon settlers in western Scotland who arrived about the same period as the Oban Azilian-Maglemosian peoples.

To sum up, it would appear that when the last traces of the Ice Age were passing away in northern and north-western England and in hilly Scotland, hunters and fishermen from the Baltic area and from modern France were settling in this country, and that among them were Cro-Magnons. Those who came across the North Sea land-bridge were probably fair and those from France were probably dark. Among the latter may have been tall Cro-Magnons with high cheek-bones. The skulls found in the MacArthur Cave, Oban, are of a type still found among the modern population in Scotland. Tall individuals with high cheek-bones are not uncommon in

Scotland and in some parts of England even in our own day.

No relics of the Azilian or Maglemosian peoples have been found in Ireland.

CHAPTER XIII

The Discovery of Agriculture

A new era was ushered in when the early people became agriculturists. As hunters and fishermen they were merely "food gatherers". They gathered such food as could be obtained—the animals they slew and the fish they caught. The number of persons who could reside in any one district was limited by the amount of food that could be gathered. Only from one to sixteen could live in a square mile. The surplus population had to migrate to new areas in search of wild animals.

When, however, cereals like barley, millet, and wheat were cultivated, the people became "food producers" as well as "food gatherers". They were able to store up a new kind of food that did not perish quickly like flesh and fish; larger numbers could then make their homes in one district without fear of starvation. Permanent villages came into existence, and the small farmers began to keep and feed domesticated animals, a thing wandering hunters could not do.

The discovery of agriculture was a most important event in the history of mankind. With that discovery, indeed, begins the story of modern civilization. The farmers had to have laws to protect individuals and their possessions. These laws had to be enforced. The leader of a community became the ruler and the judge.

It was necessary that the small farmers should till the land and sow seeds at the proper season. This meant that time had to be measured. The calendar was therefore introduced, and the calendar we are using to-day was invented in its earliest form by the pioneer farmers.

As we have seen, a number of inventions were carried into Europe from North Africa during the Hunting period. It was from that area that the Aurignacian industry came. The Solutrean industry entered Europe from the east and may have come from Asia, but the later Magdalenian industry was developed from the Aurignacian industry. The Tardenoisian industry came from North Africa, like the earlier Aurignacian.

When a large part of Europe was under ice and the reindeer lived in France, the climate in North Africa was milder and more moist than is the case at the present time. Grass and trees flourished in the Sahara, a large part of Egypt was a lake, and there were forests and grass-lands between Egypt and the Red Sea.

Evidence that early man also lived on the shores of the Egyptian lake has been found on the cliffs above the Valley of Kings' Tombs near Luxor. Their worked flints may still be picked up in large numbers. Some scientists are of opinion that groups of hunters were living in this area as far back as the First Glacial period in Europe.

When the Egyptian lake was being gradually drained by the Nile after it began to flow in increasing volume towards the sea, large quantities of rocks and gravel were deposited beneath the cliffs. Worked flints were carried down by the waters, and some of these have been found on the old river terraces.

For a long period the River Nile flowed at a much higher level than it does at present. Its bed became deeper and deeper in time. Marshes were then formed along the river banks, and in the mud carried down by the floods trees and other plants grew.

In time the hunters came down from the cliffs and began to dwell in the fertile valley. Like the European hunters, they engraved pictures of animals on the rocks.

During the Fourth Glacial period of Europe, the River Nile, having almost worn out its present bed, was laying down larger and larger quantities of mud along its banks. Year by year and century by century the mud left grew thicker and thicker. In some places the dried mud is now from fifty to sixty feet deep.

The Egyptian hunters dwelt on the river side when the mud banks began to form, and traces of them are found deep down in the " alluvial floor ". Borings which have been made near Cairo and elsewhere have led to the discovery of fragments of the pottery made by the early people.

These very ancient Egyptians buried their dead in cemeteries on the outer edge of the mud. The graves were dug in the warm dry sand. In time, however, the mud was pushed out over the sand, covering the ancient cemeteries, which now lie under cultivated land.

Part of an ancient cemetery was discovered some years ago in Naga-ed-dêr in Upper Egypt. It was found that the bodies which had been laid in the warm dry sand had been naturally mummified and so well preserved that the contents of the stomachs could be examined. Among these contents were husks of barley and millet and fragments of fish and animal bones. There can be no doubt, therefore, that these early Egyptians were agriculturists as well as hunters and fishermen.

The barley and millet, as experts have found, were native to Egypt. They were cultivated wild grasses which had been growing for thousands of years in the valley of the Nile.

The seeds of wild grasses are not very plump as a rule, but when cultivated by man, they increase in bulk.

In Egypt the barley and millet grasses were first cultivated, however, by the River Nile, which, in some respects, is the most wonderful river in the world. Each year it rises and floods a great part of the valley. Then it gradually retreats, leaving lakes and pools that form natural irrigation channels. It happens that the flood retreats just at the beginning of the cool season. Barley and millet wild grasses then shoot up in the damp soil and they grow ripe at the beginning of the hot season, when the seeds fall and are buried in the dry soil, where they remain until the river floods again and causes them to sprout.

For many centuries the River Nile had been cultivating barley and millet in this way, so that their seeds became plump enough to attract the attention of man to their value as food.

In time the first farmer began to assist the river by clearing the sand-choked irrigation channels and by forming new channels. The barley then grew in larger quantities, and the farmer and his friends, having learned a useful lesson, began to form little fields and store the water in pools so as to keep the crops irrigated. The Nile thus taught the Egyptians how to become agriculturists. At the beginning the small farmers were really the " pupils " of the Nile.

The new mode of life which was introduced when farming began made the dwellers in the Nile valley take a great interest in nature. The Nile measured the year for them. They came to know that when the river flood retreated the time had arrived to sow seeds. They also observed that when the crops were ripe, the hot season had begun. They subdivided the year into three seasons—the season of inundation, the cool season, and the hot season.

Each season was divided into four months—that is, into moon periods. A month began with the appearance of the "new moon" and ended with the last phase of the "old moon". It had three weeks, each being ten days in length. The twelve months of thirty days made up a year of 360 days. It was found, however, that the year was longer than this, and five extra days were added to each year. These were observed as festival days.

After the calendar had been in use for some centuries, it was discovered by the scholars of the time that the sun, as well as the Nile, measured the year. The solar calendar was then invented. This calendar was long afterwards introduced into Europe. It has been readjusted once or twice. It is really, however, the old Egyptian calendar that we are still using.

The dwellers in the Nile valley who introduced agriculture were of the Mediterranean race—dark-eyed and dark-haired people of medium stature and with long heads. This race had spread along the North African coast and entered Europe at the close of the Magdalenian period, and they met and mingled there with broad-headed people of medium size from Asia. These mingled peoples are known as the carriers of the Tardenoisian and Azilian tools and weapons. The long-headed people were for a considerable period in the majority.

Before agriculture could be introduced into Europe the seeds of cultivated barley, millet, and wheat had first to be obtained. Some think that the earliest supplies of these seeds were carried into southern Europe across the Italian land-bridge. After the land sank, and that "bridge" was severed by the sea, the seeds that reached Europe were carried by way of Palestine, Syria, and Asia Minor, and then across the Dardanelles, or directly across the Mediterranean in the boats of the earliest mariners.

The seeds would have been of little use unless those who brought them into Europe had formed colonies and begun to farm waste land. They had to bring with them agricultural implements as well as seeds, and the hunters who became farmers had to be instructed how to till the soil, sow the seeds, protect the fields against wild animals, and reap the crops when they were ripe.

When the crops were harvested, the colonists had to instruct the natives how to grind the cereals so as to make cakes and porridge. The cereals were also cooked and eaten whole.

The farming colonists who came from North Africa must also have introduced the laws they were accustomed to. Their villages were no doubt governed in the same way as were those they had come from.

The natural conditions in Europe are, however, different from those in North Africa. The new farms were made fertile by rain, instead of by a flooding river like the Nile. In time, the habits and methods of the European farmers had to be adapted to suit the new localities in which they had settled. New problems had to be solved in Europe, and in solving them the new communities made progress on local lines. Progress was thus forced upon them by necessity, and it was fostered by experience in the course of time.

It must be borne in mind, however, that progress began in the first place after the new agricultural mode of life was introduced into Europe. The farmers could not make a beginning until they had obtained the seeds and were instructed how to work small farms. Nor could those who obtained the seed from seafarers have obtained them at all unless boats had first been invented.

The invention of boats is dealt with in the next chapter.

CHAPTER XIV

The Invention of Boats

The discovery of how to use and produce fire, the discovery of how to work flint, and the discovery of agriculture mark important stages in the history of early man. When the boat was invented another great advance in civilization was made possible. From the first real boat was ultimately developed the sea-going ship.

At the outset we must distinguish between floats and boats. Some peoples crossed rivers and lakes by using rafts or by making skin floats. In central Asia, in our own time, natives sew up the skins of large animals, make them airtight, and inflate them. They sit on the top of these inflated skins and paddle them across a deep river.

Rafts were formed from logs of wood at an early period. In Mesopotamia the rafts were made more buoyant by tying skin-floats all round them.

The very ancient Egyptians made cigar-shaped floats by tying together bundles of reeds. Two bundles were then tied side by side, forming " double floats ", which were called " The Binding ". Some Egyptian peasants still make and use these double floats.

It was from the reed-float that the Egyptians in ancient times made the first boat.

Deris (Inflated Skins) out of the Water

The earliest known specimen of an Egyptian boat is to be seen engraved on the cliffs at el-Kab in the Nile valley. It was drawn by one of those ancient artists who carved the figures of wild animals on rock as did the Cro-Magnon hunters in Europe. This boat resembles very closely the simple river vessels which were depicted at a much later period in the tombs of the Egyptian aristocrats.

In one tomb picture three workmen are seen making a

river boat by binding the reeds together with ropes. This type of boat was also called "The Binding" because it was bound in the same way as were the double floats.

Somebody had discovered how a single reed float could be used with safety. He had apparently been studying fishes and birds, for the fore part of the vessel has a fish shape and the stern rises like the hinder part of a swimming bird.

As the inventor of the boat made use of reeds, he was able to make experiments without much trouble. He had to discover the particular shape a boat required to be so that it might float by itself and bear the weight of a man without tilting over. When he had solved the problem of balance, it was possible to make larger and heavier boats of wood.

It used to be thought that wooden boats came first. Some believed that men made their earliest boats, which are called "dug-outs", from the trunks of trees.

The specimens of boats of this kind which have been discovered are not, however, nearly so old as the reed boats of Egypt.

It has been suggested that the early people began to think about boats when they saw fallen trees carried down rivers; that a bold adventurer got on to a floating tree and sat upon it, and then found that it was possible to cross and travel down rivers by using the trunks of trees. In time, according to this theory, some man hollowed out a seat for himself on the tree trunk. He found that he could paddle with greater ease when he had done so. This led to the whole trunk being hollowed out and the first boat being invented.

The way to test this theory is to attempt to stand or sit on a floating trunk of a tree. If one tries to do such a thing, one must expect a wetting, for the tree is apt to roll round. It takes some practice to use a tree as a float. Before it can be safely depended upon it must be shaped so that it may lie steadily in the water when any weight is placed upon it. In other words, it must be given a boat shape, broad in the middle and tapering at one end.

It is unlikely that the inventor of the first boat experimented with trees when he was trying to discover what shape a boat should be so that it might have perfect balance on the water. Tree after tree would have to be shaped with small

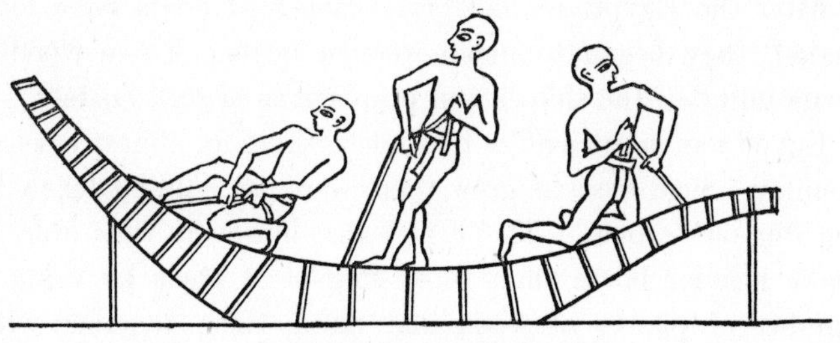

Egyptian "Binding"

tools of stone, and a man might spend his whole life-time working very hard and yet never discover the proper dimensions of a boat.

A very reasonable view is that early man never saw a boat in a tree until after a boat of light material had first been invented.

In Egypt there can be no doubt that the reed boat called " The Binding " comes first. The boat-builders in that country discovered the proportions and shape that a boat should have by experimenting with reeds. Then they shaped hollow reed boats and made them watertight by covering them with pitch.

It was a boat of this type which the mother of Moses made when the Pharaoh of Egypt commanded that every Hebrew boy should be drowned in the Nile as soon as he was born. The boat is referred to in the Bible as an "ark". It is told that the mother of Moses hid her baby for three months. "And when she could no longer hide him, she took for him an ark of bulrushes (reeds), and daubed it with slime and with pitch, and put the child therein; and she laid it in the flags by the river's brink." (*Exodus*, ii, 3.)

After the Egyptians had been using reed boats for a long period, they began to make wooden boats. These wooden boats imitated the shapes and proportions of reed boats.

Egypt was in ancient as in modern times an almost treeless country. Such trees as grew there were not suitable for making dug-out canoes. The Egyptians, however, were able to make heavier boats than those shaped of reeds by using a number of planks of wood and fixing them together with wooden pins. It may be that they also used skins which were sewn over a framework of wood.

In time the Egyptian boat-builders made boats which could be used with safety on the seas, as they had been for long on the River Nile. Then the seafarers sailed round the coast to Palestine and Syria and discovered the forests of Lebanon.

Trees were cut down on the Syrian coast and bound together as rafts, and these were drifted down to the Nile. After wood was thus imported into Egypt, the boat-builders made "dug-outs" in imitation of the earlier reed boats. Later on they made boats by cutting long planks from the trees, but that kind of work was not possible until metal saws had been invented. Small planks were, however, got by splitting the trees with wedges and dressing the planks with flint adzes.

Before heavy vessels were turned out in the Egyptian shipbuilding yards, the mast and sail were introduced. The earliest masts, as is shown by pottery pictures, were not very high, and the sails appear to have been screens of dried reeds.

A tall single mast could not have been easily fixed up in a reed boat, and if it were not made fast securely a gust of wind would blow it down.

The earliest long masts, as is found in the tomb pictures, were double or tripod, and attached to the bulwarks. They were kept from being blown overboard by ropes, backstays and forestays. When boats were decked, single masts became common. These were usually lowered when not in use.

The ancient mariners who ventured on the Mediterranean began in time to make long voyages. They followed the coasts as a rule, but there were some who did not fear to lose sight of land and were guided by the birds that migrate across the sea. In time the mariners made night voyages, steering with the aid of the stars.

At an early period daring seafarers from the Mediterranean made voyages round the coasts of the countries we now know as Spain, Portugal, and France. Some crossed to the great island that was ultimately called Britain. Once this sea-route had been opened, voyages were made so as to procure supplies of things that were required, including tin, copper, lead, and even gold.

About seventeen ancient boats were discovered in Glasgow and its neighbourhood during the latter part of the eighteenth century and the early part of the nineteenth century. Some were lying at more than twenty feet above the present sea-level. One was sticking in sand below a Glasgow street at an angle of forty-five degrees. Another was lying upside down as if it had capsized. It had been built of oaken planks which were fastened by pins of oak to the ribs. The bow was carved and the stern was of triangular shape. Another boat built of planks was found near it. The rest of the boats were dug-outs which had been shaped from the trunks of oak trees. Some had been dressed as smoothly as the Polynesian canoes which are shaped with stone adzes.

In one of these Glasgow boats was found a beautifully polished axe or adze of greenstone. Another boat had a plug of cork, and must therefore have come from an area where cork trees grow—that is, from Spain or from southern France, or from Italy.

A big dug-out was found at Brigg in Lincolnshire in 1886 while workmen were digging on the site of a new gasometer. It had been shaped from the trunk of an oak tree, and was 48 feet 6 inches long, nearly 6 feet wide, and 2 feet 9 inches deep. The bottom of this boat is flat and the bow rounded.

Another dug-out was found in 1883 near the River Atun in Sussex. It is 35 feet long, 4 feet broad, and 2 feet deep. A third boat found at Rother in Kent is 63 feet long and 5 feet broad. In York museum there is a "dug out" which is about 25 feet in length.

These and other dug-outs appear to have all been shaped by workmen who used stone adzes.

The Glasgow boats, which lay fully twenty feet above the present sea-level, cannot be dated with certainty. They must have reached the Clyde, however, during the period when the last land movement was taking place, that is, when Scotland was gradually rising and the land in the south of England was gradually sinking.

Some scientists think that this land movement began about 3000 B.C. Before that date the Egyptian sailors had reached Crete and Cyprus, where colonies were established. There were also colonies of seafarers on the coasts of Palestine, Syria, Asia Minor, Greece, and Italy. From some of these settlements seafarers went to southern Spain, where copper and silver were found. It may be that the seafarers who reached the Clyde had set out from an ancient port of Spain.

Some early boats were, as stated, made of skins which were stretched on a frame of wickerwork. These were excellent boats of their kind for rough seas. Boats of this kind continued in use round our coasts until comparatively recently. The skins were tanned and sewn in two or three layers, and, after being stretched over the wickerwork, were covered with pitch. We still speak of the "seams" and the "skin" of a boat. Some of the old skin boats had decks and half-decks and masts for sails.

Boats were built and used at a very early period on the Red Sea as well as on the Mediterranean. The mariners coasted round Arabia and reached the Persian Gulf, and, in time, round to India and beyond.

A very interesting fact about the ancient boats is that they had eyes painted or carved on their prows. Eyes are still painted on some Maltese boats and on fishing-boats in the Outer Hebrides, as well as on native boats in India, Ceylon, China, &c.

Experts in boat-building are of opinion that the boat was invented in one particular area, and most of them think that area was Egypt. They hold that the Egyptian boat was gradually introduced all over the world, just as in our own day has been the railway engine, which was invented in England.

CHAPTER XV

The Prehistoric Egyptians

During the Fourth Glacial and the Post-glacial epochs the early hunters who lived in Egypt had a less severe struggle for existence than had the cave-dwellers in Europe. The climate of the Nile valley was genial and large tracts which are now desert wastes were habitable. Game was plentiful and there was an abundance of fish in the Nile.

The evidence of the great antiquity of human activities in Egypt is of a peculiarly interesting kind. As stated in Chapter XIII, flint tools have been found in large numbers on the ancient river terraces in the valley, which were occupied by the hunters' camps when the Nile flowed at a very much higher level than it does in our day. Occasionally these worked flints were washed down the " wadis " (ancient water-courses) by floods and deposited on the river banks. They were deeply embedded in masses of mud and " rock rubbish ", and in the course of ages these masses were hardened by cementing material into conglomerate rock, for which a popular name is " pudding stone ". Out of the conglomerate, which in some areas covers thousands of square yards, one can nowadays, using a hammer and chisel, chip out worked flints similar to those found on the upper terraces. As conglomerate takes thousands of years to form, one thus gets a good idea of the great age of the early Egyptian flint tools.

On rock faces in the Nile valley and even out on the desert one occasionally finds incised drawings which were made with pointed flint " gravers ". Professor Breasted was once informed by a native of Abu Simbel that there was an ancient temple in the northern Nubian desert. This man led the American scientist far out into the sandy wastes lying to the west of the Nile, and it was found that what had been called an ancient temple was a natural rock formation pierced by an arched " doorway " which had been scooped out by the action of water in very ancient times. There were, however, traces of early man at this interesting site. On the rock were carved " two boats, two giraffes, two ostriches, and a number of smaller animals ". Professor Breasted reminds us that " the giraffe has been extinct in Egypt from very remote times ", and he adds that " it is possible the hunters of the Pleistocene Age have left these records in the Sahara ". When the giraffes were wandering about in that area which is now a sandy desolation, there must have been vegetation to provide them with the food they required as well as water to drink. It is also of importance to note that boats had been invented before the giraffes disappeared from the Nile valley and its neighbourhood.

Reference has already been made to the drawing of an ancient Egyptian boat on the cliffs at el-Kab in the Nile valley. The antiquity of this and other rock pictures is proved by the fact that they are covered with what has been called " desert varnish ", which is of a dark brown colour. This rock polish has been caused either by the action of moisture and heat throughout long ages or by wind-blown dust which has adhered to the surface of the cliffs. The polishing or " varnishing " of the darkened rocks has been a very slow and gradual process. This is shown by the state of the inscriptions cut on the rocks about 5000 years ago, for these bear little trace of the " desert varnish ". The rock pictures of the ancient hunting peoples of the Nile valley must be some hundreds of years older than the early inscriptions referred to. Thus " desert varnish " provides us with evidence of the great age of the Egyptian rock drawings, as does the stalagmite which covers some of the Cro-Magnon cave pictures in western Europe.

During the Fourth Glacial epoch the River Nile was laying down the soil which was ultimately to be cultivated by the inhabitants of Egypt. As excavations and borings through the alluvium have shown that pottery is to be found in the deepest layers, it is evident that when the hunters descended from the ancient terraces they began to make clay vessels to serve as cooking-pots, water-pots, and bowls.

Nature may have suggested to the early Egyptians how to make clay pots, as it suggested to him how to cultivate barley. The river brings down clay and the hot sun bakes it hard. Lumps of baked clay could be used to build houses. The hunters may have thus been accustomed to use " natural bricks " before they imitated nature by manufacturing bricks in suitable shapes. Occasionally whirling water will scoop out holes in lumps of clay, and when these lumps are sun-baked they can be used to carry water. Once the early inventor observed that clay could be used to make useful vessels, the craft of the potter was introduced.

After agriculture was introduced the population of Egypt increased greatly. Hunting and fishing were still continued, but the people were not wholly dependent on animals and fish for food. An era of progress then set in. It became possible for the inhabitants of Egypt to advance on new lines, not because they had more brain power than the Cro-Magnon hunters of Europe, or because they were more vigorous, but chiefly because they lived in an area where nature was an instructor and the climate was genial. Once they began to grow corn, they no longer lived, as did hunting peoples, on the edge of starvation. They had more leisure in which to make experiments and to discover things. Withal, they were forced by sheer necessity to solve some problems. The River Nile had to be crossed, and boats were required and had to be invented. Their country was a narrow one—just two strips of land on either side of the Nile, the desert sands having wiped out all vegetation which formerly grew on the Sahara and the area between the Nile and the Red Sea.

Egyptian Domesticated Dog with Collar

It was domesticated in Egypt at end of the Quaternary Period and in Europe later.

The domestication of animals came later than the introduction of agriculture. It is possible that the first step in this direction was taken when the farmers found it necessary to protect their fields against the ravages of cows, boars, asses, &c. They did not erect fences, but appear to have caught many animals by driving them into enclosures. An ancient relief found in the pyramid temple of Sahure, and dating back to the middle of the twenty-eighth century B.C., shows a hunting enclosure full of wild animals, many of which had been wounded.

Nothing tames animals like hunger. The wild deer of the Scottish Highlands become so tame during the winter season that they are " hand-fed " by gamekeepers. No doubt, many of the animals caught by the Egyptians similarly ceased to fear man when hungry, and accepted food readily in an enclosure. Their young could be reared in captivity and would be quite tame.

From old reliefs we find that cows, asses, horned sheep, and goats were kept by the Egyptians and that they had also domesticated geese and ducks. All these animals were native to North Africa. The cattle were of the long-horned type and are known to have lived in a wild state in northern Egypt and westward along the North African coast to the country we now know as Algiers. The theory that the earliest domesticated animals in Egypt came from Asia is not favoured by those who realize how difficult it would have been to drive flocks and herds across the waterless desert of Sinai. Cattle, sheep, and goats would have perished in a few days on the hot, sandy wastes.

In time, as agriculture was developed, the Egyptians trained the oxen to draw the plough, which was, to begin with, formed like the ordinary wooden hoes used to break up the ground. Asses were trained to carry burdens. Cows and goats were milked and their flesh was eaten.

Much information regarding the customs and industries of the inhabitants of Egypt is found in the ancient graves. It was believed that the dead required food, and it was customary to place a number of pottery vessels beside them. In the oldest known graves half a dozen jars and bowls were laid beside the dead, who were placed in a crouching position with the arms bent and the hands in front of the faces. The body was wrapped in the skin of an animal, or in linen, or covered with a reed mat. Occasionally the body was protected by a big clay vessel placed with the rim downwards, or a clay coffin was provided. Some graves were lined with brick or wood, but most of them were just sand pits.

Among the articles placed in the graves for the use of the dead were tools and weapons, and also the ornaments which were worn by the living as amulets. The habit of using face paint for magical purposes, and to protect the eyes from the glare of the sun by making a dark line under them, was common in very early times. In some graves the archæologists have found palettes of slate on which malachite (a green ore of copper) was ground with the aid of a small pebble so as to provide a pigment for eyelid paint.

There are no inscriptions of the early period under review, and the story of progress has to be pieced together by studying the articles discovered in the graves. It is found that the Egyptians became very skilled as artisans. Their hand-made pottery was given graceful shapes. When a pot was baked on a fire and placed rim downwards, the part which was sunk in the charcoal became black. This " black top " pottery, as it is called, remained in use for a long period. As it was found that pure clay is apt to crack when baked on a fire, the potters learned, in time, to introduce limestone or quartz so as to prevent cracking. After a long period it was discovered that a glassy paste could be prepared by fusing sand, soda, and a metallic oxide, and the pots were then glazed. The Egyptians were the inventors of glazed pottery.

As workers of flint, the Egyptians surpassed all ancient peoples. Their flint knives with ripple-flakes were not only of beautiful shape but were given sharp edges by means of minute and delicate flaking. Handles of ivory, wood, and bone were used. Some of the knives had handles of gold, and these may have been used for religious purposes.

All the information that has been gleaned regarding the ancient Egyptians of the early period comes from the Nile valley. The Delta region has so far yielded no traces of the activities of the pioneer agriculturists, or any graves. Owing to the vast quantities of mud deposited by the Nile branches in that area, the relics of early man which may have survived lie at a great depth. It was, however, in Lower Egypt that the calendar was introduced and the river boatmen first ventured on the Mediterranean. The Lower Egyptians must therefore have made great progress in civilization, and been at least as far advanced as the inhabitants of Middle and Upper Egypt during the early period under review.

Egyptian history begins with the conquest of Lower Egypt by the united peoples of Middle and Upper Egypt and the founding of the first dynasty by King Menes. The long period prior to this conquest is called the " pre-dynastic period ".

During the latter part of the pre-dynastic period Egypt was divided into small states. These then became grouped into two rival kingdoms—that of Upper Egypt and that of Lower Egypt.

When, after the conquest, a single pharaoh ruled over all Egypt, the united kingdom became rich and powerful. The pharaoh was regarded as a god and the masses of the people revered him and served him.

During the early dynastic period the great pyramids of Egypt were erected. The work entailed could never have been carried out if the people had not been disciplined to obey the commands of their rulers as a religious duty.

The largest of the pyramids, situated near Cairo, are the greatest piles of stone masonry ever erected by man.

Shortly before 3000 B.C. the first grave of hewn stones was

Photo. Bonfils

THE STEP PYRAMID OF SAKKARA

constructed for a pharaoh. In the course of a century rapid progress was made in working stone, and the first pyramid was erected at Sakkara as a tomb for a pharaoh who was named Zoser. During the next four hundred years a large number of pyramids were built.

Egypt was the country of the earliest stone-masons, and the first country in which the people were united under the rule of great autocratic kings whose word was law. Thousands of labourers and artisans devoted their lives to the work of providing vast tombs for their rulers, and artists and sculptors were trained and employed to provide pictures and statues for tombs and temples. Great progress was made in the arts and crafts, because the people were thoroughly organized and disciplined to serve their rulers.

The progress achieved was made possible by the situation of Egypt. It was protected on the east and west by barren deserts and on the north by the Mediterranean Sea. Invaders from Asia had to cross the almost waterless desert of Sinai, and could be held in check with comparative ease so long as a pharaoh remained powerful and had a strong army at his command.

Nature, which had taught so much to the Egyptians, thus afforded them protection against rivals and plunderers, and their civilization developed rapidly on local lines. As the population increased, larger and larger areas of desert had to be irrigated and cultivated so as to provide an abundance of food. It was because the harvests were so plenteous that the pharaoh and his nobles could command the labour of large numbers of subjects and provide food for them.

Egypt required much from other countries, and especially wood and metals. The supplies were not, however, imported by Egyptian merchants. The pharaohs sent expeditions to Sinai to work the copper-mines, and they sent fleets of ships to the Syrian coast to obtain the cedar of Lebanon. For many centuries the Government controlled the trade of Egypt, exporting and importing large quantities of goods. When foreign traders crossed the Mediterranean, or came from Asia across the desert of Sinai, it was not with private traders but with the Government officials that they conducted business.

The progress achieved in Egypt may be said to have been due in large measure to the intelligent control of the most tyrannical Government the world has ever seen.

CHAPTER XVI

The Sumerians of Mesopotamia

The second great centre of old-world civilization was the valley of the Tigris and Euphrates in Lower Mesopotamia. This country was anciently known as Babylonia and Chaldea, and in our own time is called Iraq.

Like Egypt, this valley is of river origin. The plain was gradually formed in the course of long ages by the mud carried down by the rivers Tigris and Euphrates. During the Fourth Glacial epoch, when the Nile was beginning to deposit mud along its sandy banks, the Persian Gulf reached far inland to the vicinity of the modern city of Baghdad. We do not know at what rate the valley was formed by river mud. The land rose after the passing of the last phase of the Ice Age, and for a time the "filling up" process may have been rapid. We know, however, that since the time of Alexander the Great, who died about 2250 years ago, the seashore has been pushed back by river deposits and accumulations of drifting sand a distance of nearly fifty miles.

Eridu, the most ancient city in Lower Mesopotamia, is now a heap of ruins situated about 125 miles from the head of the Persian Gulf. Originally, as its name indicates, it was a "seaport". Excavations have revealed that when it was first built it stood on a limestone ridge on the shore of an inland lake which was connected with the Gulf by a river branch. The traditions associated with it point to its having been founded by seafarers who introduced a civilization which had origin elsewhere.

We do not know definitely who those seafarers were. They appear to have been related to the early settlers in Elam in south-western Persia who worked flint and obsidian, made use of copper, and manufactured pottery. The oldest finds at Susa have been discovered at a great depth, but it is difficult to make an estimate of the rate of accumulation at this site as compared with other sites because everywhere there were local variations. Dust-storms must be taken into account, and these did not have the same results at various periods at one place or in different places. Similarly water-laid deposits varied from time to time in one particular area and in other areas.

As in Egypt, there were at an early period in Lower Mesopotamia and in other parts of western Asia, representatives of the long-headed, short-statured men of the Mediterranean race. These appear to have been the pioneer settlers. Like the pre-dynastic Egyptians, the earliest settlers in Susa manufactured finely-woven linen. Their pottery is so fine, however, that archæologists believe they possessed the potter's wheel, which was not known in Egypt until early dynastic times.

From some area in the north a people whom we know as the Sumerians migrated into Lower Mesopotamia and Elam, and absorbed the earlier people. Their skulls were of mixed type, indicating that they were a "blend" of broad-heads and long-heads. The earliest known portraits of this people show that they had prominent noses, and that they had eyebrows sloping towards the outer corners of their eyes as have many northern European peoples at the present day. They shaved their faces and heads, and they wore woollen kilts, their shoulders being bare. The gowns of women were suspended from the left shoulder.

Lower Mesopotamia is referred to in the Bible as "Shinar". This is the Hebrew rendering of the name we know as "Sumer" (pronounced *shoo'mer*). It is customary nowadays to refer to the ancient people of Sumer as the Sumerians.

The Sumerians spoke an agglutinative language as do the Basques of western Europe in our own time. We do not know whether or not an agglutinative language was spoken in Lower Egypt in pre-dynastic times, or in Crete before Greek times. The dynastic language of Egypt was not an agglutinative one, but appears to have had relations with the Semitic group of languages.

The Sumerians adopted the agricultural mode of life which had been introduced into Lower Mesopotamia, and they practised the irrigation system which the Nile had taught to the early agriculturists in Egypt. Barley, wheat, and millet were grown, and fruit-yielding trees were cultivated.

Stone was used for building in Eridu, and suitable stone was found there. Elsewhere in the Lower Mesopotamian plain bricks were manufactured for building houses and temples.

At an early period a Semitic people, who did not shave their heads and faces, settled in the northern part of the Lower Mesopotamian plain. We know them as the Akkadians—the people of Akkad. In historic times the plain below Baghdad was known as " the land of Sumer and Akkad ".

In prehistoric times the Sumerians and Akkadians built small cities of brick houses, and these, with the agricultural areas adjoining them, were independent states. As the country was more open to attack by invaders than was Egypt, the Sumerians had often to engage in war and they became efficient warriors. The closely-formed battalion of spearmen, known as the phalanx, had its origin in Sumeria.

Not only did the Sumerians engage in warfare against intruders, but they fought among themselves. One city state attacked another and conquered it. Groups of city states were from time to time formed by conquerors, and rival groups struggled for supreme power.

Pictorial art did not make such progress in Sumer and Akkad as it did in Egypt. The Sumerians, however, were an enterprising people and became industrious craftsmen and traders. They had to go long distances to procure wood, stone for statues, &c., and metals, and they founded colonies in northern Mesopotamia and in Asia Minor. Sumerian civilization spread from the colonies over wide areas and influenced the Semitic and other peoples.

A system of pictorial writing was introduced in Sumeria at a very early period. The Egyptians had similarly, to begin with, a system of picture signs which was developed into alphabetic signs. In the separated countries the process of writing, however, followed different lines. The Egyptians manufactured from the papyrus reed a parchment (the earliest paper) on which they traced alphabetic characters with a pen. In Sumer clay tablets were used, and the signs, developed from pictures, were made by pressing a wedge-shaped stylus on the soft clay. This system of writing is called "cuneiform", from the Latin word *cuneus*, a wedge. The people of Crete also used clay tablets for their records, and the later scholars of Rome wrote on wax tablets. Modern paper is remotely of Egyptian origin, as is also the modern pen. The Chinese system of writing betrays the influence of ancient Sumeria.

Once the system of writing was introduced in the ancient world, there were local developments in various areas. The Greek and Roman alphabets were late developments of systems which had been improved and simplified by merchants and scholars in the course of the ages.

There are indications that pre-dynastic Egypt and Sumeria were brought into touch. The peoples of both countries visited Lebanon for timber, and they appear to have met there and to have met also on the shores of the Red Sea and perhaps in Arabia. The mace heads of the two peoples were similar, and the cylinder seal, which was used by Sumerian merchants, was introduced into Egypt. There are withal resemblances between certain burial customs and between some art objects and symbols and there are links in religion. Both peoples, as has been indicated, had a similar system of agriculture, and both had domesticated animals.

Some hold that the Egyptians were the originators of agriculture and copper-working, while others hold that they were indebted to the people of Mesopotamia for the main

SUMERIAN DAIRY SCENE IN THE FOURTH MILLENNIUM, B.C.

Part of an inlaid frieze of white limestone and black paste discovered at Tell-el-Obeid by the Joint Expedition of the British Museum and the University Museum, Philadelphia. *By courtesy of C. Leonard Woolley*

elements of civilization. The problem is a difficult one, but the fact cannot be overlooked that there was continuous development in Egypt from the remote Age when the Nile began to deposit soil in the valley. The Egyptians cultivated barley and millet native to Egypt and domesticated North African animals.

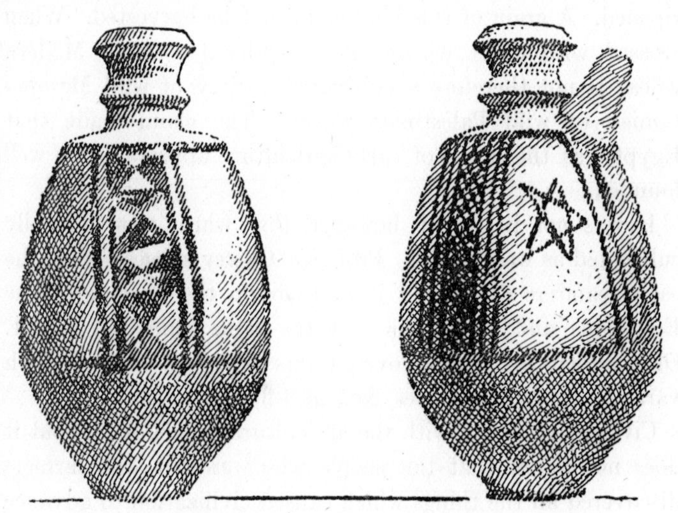

Sumerian Painted Jar of about 3500 B.C., discovered containing Wheat by Professor Stephen Langdon in Mesopotamia

Reproduced by permission of Professor Stephen Langdon.

In Egypt the Nile floods retreat at the beginning of the cool season, and this was favourable for the natural cultivation of barley, as has been shown. In Mesopotamia, on the other hand, the flooding of the rivers Tigris and Euphrates takes place at the beginning of the hot season and was not favourable for the cultivation of barley. The system of irrigation practised in Mesopotamia had been developed elsewhere, and the first thing necessary to make it suit local needs was to erect banks to keep back the floods, so that the channels might be formed and protected. It used to be thought that the wheat cultivated by the Sumerians was the wild wheat of Mesopotamia and Palestine. It has been proved of late, however, that this wheat sheds from its ear each grain as it is ripened. A grain of this kind could not be harvested. When crossed with other wheats, it is rendered sterile. Modern wheat is not therefore a cultivated variety of wild Mesopotamian or wild Palestinian wheat. The claim made that Egypt was the home of early agriculture appears to be well founded.

It was not in Egypt, however, that wheat was naturally cultivated as was barley. Professor Cherry suggests that the early seafarers discovered it in Delos in the Cyclades. The Egyptians and Sumerians had the same name for wheat. Once agriculture was discovered experiments were made with various cereals, vegetables, &c., in different areas.

Civilization began with the agricultural mode of life, but it does not follow that the people who were the first farmers discovered all the things which caused civilization to advance in early times. Important inventions were made by individuals in different areas into which agriculture had been introduced, and when different communities were brought into contact in districts visited by their seafarers and overland expeditions, discoveries, inventions, and ideas were, no doubt, interchanged. At this time of day it is difficult to tell whether a particular object common to the Sumerians and Egyptians was invented in Egypt or in Mesopotamia. A useful article was in ancient as in modern times quickly adopted, no matter in what area it had origin.

In Egypt and Mesopotamia the arts and crafts of civilization were flourishing long before agriculture was introduced into western Europe, and while the peoples in that area were still hunters and fishermen thinly scattered over wide districts.

The chapters that follow tell how civilization reached and spread through Europe.

CHAPTER XVII

How Civilization reached Europe

One of the most interesting stories of the ancient world has been pieced together of recent years with the aid of the wonderful discoveries made in the Ægean area—that is, in Crete, in southern Greece, at Troy, at the mouth of the Dardanelles, and on the islands known as the Cyclades, which are sprinkled over the Ægean Sea between the Greek mainland and the western coast of Asia Minor. It was in this area that the basis of modern European civilization was laid. Long before the civilization of Greece came into existence—before the people we know as the Greeks had entered the land which they were to make so famous—the Ægean area was peopled by agriculturists and seafarers who were enterprising and progressive. They built cities which were " hives of industry ", they set out on voyages of exploration towards the lands of the western Mediterranean area, and they sailed up the Dardanelles to explore the regions round the Black Sea.

It was from the Ægean area that a great part of Europe received the new civilization which enticed the hunting tribes to settle down in organized communities to till the land, to engage in trade, and build boats with which to visit other countries.

The chief centre of Ægean civilization was the island of Crete. For long ages it had been uninhabited because the Palæolithic hunters were unable to reach it. After boats were invented, however, groups of seafarers arrived on the island, and some built small round huts of wattles and clay with floors of stone, while others erected rectangular houses of undressed stone. They engaged in hunting and fishing. Among the remains of the food they ate have been found the bones of cattle, sheep, pigs, and hares, and also sea-shells. As they had domesticated animals, they must have come from areas into which agriculture had been introduced, for the early farmers were the first to tame wild animals.

The pioneers in Crete appear to have practised agriculture but not to any great extent. They had no grinding-mills and may have cooked their barley whole, and as they had no sickles, they may have plucked the grain out of the ground instead of cutting it.

Perhaps the manners and customs of the early Cretans resembled those of the people of the isolated island of St. Kilda, which was visited by the Scottish traveller, M. Martin, in the seventeenth century. Martin tells that the St. Kildans of his time not only caught fish and sea-birds for food but had little farms. "They sow very thick," he wrote, "and have a proportionable growth; they pluck all their bear (barley) by the roots in handfuls, both for the sake of their houses, which they thatch with it, and their cows which they take in during the winter. . . . The barley is the largest produced in all the western isles; they use no plough but a kind of crooked spade; their harrows are of wood as are the teeth in the front also, and all the rest supplied only with long tangles of sea-ware tied to the harrow by the small ends; the roots hanging loose behind, scatter the clods broken by the wooden teeth." The St. Kildans had little cows, horned sheep, and some ponies.

Martin tells how the Hebrideans prepared their corn for food:

"A woman, sitting down, takes a handful of corn, holding it by the stalks in her left hand, and then sets fire to the ears, which are presently in a flame. She has a stick in her right hand, which she manages very dexterously, beating off the grains at the very instant when the husk is quite burnt. . . . The corn may be so dressed, winnowed, ground, and baked, within an hour after reaping from the ground."

The custom of preparing corn for food only when it was wanted must have been a very ancient one, for the Greek traveller, Poseidonius, who was born about 135 B.C., tells of a district in ancient Britain "where the people have mean habitations constructed for the most part of rushes or sticks, and their harvest consists in cutting off the ears of corn and storing them in pits underground: they take out each day the corn which has been longest stored and dress the ears for food."

Before grinding-mills came into use, the grain was pounded on a slab of stone or a hollow in a rock with a stone held in the right hand.

The earliest settlers in Crete made pottery of a coarse kind for cooking and storing food. Their women were spinners and weavers, as we know, because their bobbins and spindle weights have been found. Tools were made of stone, bone, and horn. They had no metal tools, but they made arrow-heads, knives, and razors of obsidian, a natural glass of volcanic origin which when split in flakes has a very sharp edge. They obtained the obsidian from the island of Melos, which lies between Crete and the coast of Greece. The seafarers must, therefore, have made regular voyages to obtain supplies of obsidian.

It is not known where these earliest Cretan settlers came from. Some may have reached the island from the North African coast and others from Asia Minor, cruising among the numerous small islands of the Cyclades where one is never out of sight of land.

For many centuries the Cretans lived their simple lives with little change, just like the St. Kildans on their lonely island in the north-western Hebrides, which cannot be approached by small boats except in the summer season.

Some time before 3000 B.C., however, large numbers of colonists reached Crete from Egypt. They were much more advanced in civilization than were the natives, and they had tools and weapons of copper. They made Crete their permanent home, laying the foundations of the civilization which Sir Arthur Evans has named the Minoan, after King Minos, who, according to Greek tradition, ruled over the island.

It is believed that for some time there was a steady stream of migration from the delta coast to Crete. Apparently it was caused chiefly by the wars which had long been waged in Egypt. That country had for many centuries been divided into petty states. In time, as told in Chapter XV, one state conquered another until there were two main groups forming the rival kingdoms of Lower (or Northern) Egypt and Upper (or Southern) Egypt. The memory of this early division was preserved during the whole period of ancient Egyptian civilization, for Egypt was always referred to as the " Two Lands ".

A few centuries before 3000 B.C. the armies of Upper Egypt gradually conquered Lower Egypt. According to Egyptian tradition the final stage of the conquest was carried through by King Menes, who ruled supreme over the "Two Lands". It may be that when Menes won his final victory, many of the nobles of Lower Egypt preferred to settle in another land rather than live under the rule of the conqueror. Others were likely to follow them as favourable reports were received regarding the experiences of the settlers in Crete. No doubt, rebellions broke out from time to time in Lower Egypt, and when these were suppressed the leaders and their armies would be forced to migrate across the Mediterranean to escape arrest and punishment.

Crete was not the only country which received large numbers of new settlers at this period. Southern Greece, the islands of the Cyclades, and parts of Asia Minor, including Troy on the south side of the entrance to the Dardanelles, were all occupied by new-comers. We know that the immigrants did not come from the north, because there is no trace of them among the remains of Thessaly in northern Greece. There were also settlers on Cyprus and on the coasts of Syria and Palestine. In all these areas copper was introduced, and cutting tools were made of that metal, while gold and silver were used for ornaments or amulets. Flint, obsidian, and hard stone were still used for tools and arrow-heads and continued in use for a long time. Agriculture of a more advanced kind than had for long been practised in Crete was adopted all through the area occupied by the new settlers.

The Egyptians who made their homes in Crete were able to establish a free state, or several free states, safely beyond the reach of the pharaoh. Having fled from the tyranny established by Menes, they appear to have appreciated to the full the freedom they enjoyed in a new country. It is interesting to find how the Minoans (as they are called by modern writers) fostered the spirit of freedom. They built small towns in which the citizens had more liberty than was enjoyed in Egypt. No pharaoh could force them to provide free labour for several months each year to erect great pyramids and temples. In the Egyptian cities there were large slum areas in which the workers lived in miserable huts of clay. In Crete there were substantial houses of stone, each with several rooms, and there were small workshops in which artisans plied their trades and profited from them. The Egyptian artisans were kept in a state of semi-slavery by the pharaoh, the nobles, and priests; the Cretan artisans were small traders.

The spirit of liberty which prevailed in Crete can be detected in Minoan art, the best of which is devoid of the formalism of the art of Egypt. The artists and sculptors of Egypt were constantly employed by the priests, and their products had a religious significance. In Crete the eyes of the artists were open to the beauties of nature in their fields and gardens, in the woodlands and on the shores and in the sea. Their pottery and the walls of their houses were decorated with objects of natural beauty.

Although the refugees and other settlers in Crete introduced the elements of Egyptian civilization and were influenced also in time by the civilization of Mesopotamia, they were never slavish imitators. They made progress in an atmosphere of freedom on their sea-girt island, facing new problems and solving them in their own way. The island had its own needs and these had to be faced and provided for.

Several small towns were established, and it was necessary

Photo. Giraudon

EGYPTIAN PEASANTS PLOUGHING

From a relief in the tomb of Ti, Sakkara (27–26th century B.C.) The hieroglyphs behind the ploughman are descriptive of the scene and read, "Turning in (the grain) with the plough". Above the figures the inscription is "Hi! beneath you, you two workers"

that these should be connected with roads. This was a necessity which was scarcely known in Egypt. In that country the River Nile was the "highway" along which traffic passed from town to town on rafts, barges, and sailing-boats. The only well-made roads were those laid between quarries and the river, between the river and a large building in course of construction, and from the royal palace to a temple.

The Cretans were the first people who had a complex system of roads for traffic. One road ran from Knossos (near Candia) on the north side of the island to Phæstos in the south. Other roads were connected with it, running eastward to the small towns of Mallia and Gournia, and from Gournia to the eastern ports of Palaikastro and Zakro. Portions of roadway laid bare at Knossos show that, in time, the Minoans made a great advance in road construction. They laid a bottom of stones which was covered with concrete and earth. Bridges of stone were erected over small streams. When the Minoans founded towns in southern Greece, one of them was known as "Mycenæ of the broad ways". After the Hellenic peoples took possession of Greece they found and used a fine system of highways which they never improved upon. Ultimately the Romans became the chief makers of roads in Europe.

The Minoans also introduced a wonderful drainage system, and they laid pipes to carry water-supplies from a distance.

In the next chapter the story of Minoan progress is given in outline. As the scripts used on the island in ancient times cannot be read, it is not possible to throw a full light on all the problems which arise.

CHAPTER XVIII

The Ocean Kings of Crete

In the records of ancient Egypt the Minoans of Crete are referred to chiefly as the Keftiu (" peoples of the sea "), but this term does not appear to have been confined to them alone, for it was applied to other seafarers as well. The Cretans were, however, for a long period the chief sea-traders who reached Egypt to sell their goods and make purchases to carry home.

The earliest Cretans who traded with Egypt were settled at Phæstos in the south side of Crete. In the *Odyssey* (Book III), the Greek epic by the poet Homer, we get a glimpse of the perils faced on the southern coast of Crete by early mariners. It is told that part of a fleet of " dark-prowed ships " was driven by the " shrill winds " and " swelling waves " towards " the steep shore ", where a gale casts big billows " against the left headland towards Phæstos ", and that " a small rock keeps back the great waters ". Some of the ships were wrecked, but five escaped, for " the wind and waves carried them nigh to Egypt ".

In another part of the *Odyssey* (Book XIX) the poet sings of " the land called Crete in the midst of the wine-dark sea ", which has many cities, the chief of which is Knossos. He tells of a hero who when on his voyage to Troy was caught in a storm. " The mighty wind drove him to Crete ", and he sought refuge in one of " the havens hard to win, scarcely escaping the tempest ". There for twelve days " the north wind penned " the sailors.

A vivid account of a storm in the eastern Mediterranean is

given in the Bible (*Acts of the Apostles*, chap. xxvii). Paul set out in a ship to go to Italy, " meaning to sail by the coasts ". He was, however, transferred to another ship and it sailed towards Crete. Paul advised the Roman centurion to winter in a haven on the island coast, but the master and owner of the ship wished to push on to another haven. Suddenly a storm came on:

"And when the ship was caught and could not bear up into the wind we let her drive."

The writer of the " Acts " tells that the vessel was tossed about for a fortnight. At length the island of Melita was reached. An attempt was made to beach the ship, but some distance from the shore she grounded on a bank. " The fore-part stuck fast " and " the hinder-part was broken with the violence of the waves ". Some of the men swam ashore, and the rest reached safety, " some on boards and some on broken pieces of the ship ".

These extracts serve to remind us of the perils which the early seafarers of Crete had to face when on voyages to and from other lands. They became expert navigators, but there must have been many disasters at sea. The strongest Cretan ships were built of cedar wood, as we gather from Egyptian and Greek records, and the Cretans not only transported cedar from Lebanon for their own use but also on occasion supplied it to the Egyptians. The drifting of big rafts of cedar logs from the Syrian coast was an imposing task for the early navigators. An early Egyptian pharaoh, named Snefru, who died before 2900 B.C., found it necessary to send a fleet of no fewer than forty ships to bring cedar from Lebanon.

Relics of the ancient Egypto-Cretan commercial relations

have been brought to light. Cretan objects found in Egypt and Egyptian objects found in Crete make it possible to date the periods of Minoan civilization. Sir Arthur Evans has divided what archæologists call the "pre-history" of the island into three main periods. These are the Early Minoan, the Middle Minoan, and the Late Minoan periods. Each has been subdivided and dated as follows:

Period.	Probable Date B.C.
Early Minoan I	3400–2800
Early Minoan II	2800–2400
Early Minoan III	2400–2100
Middle Minoan I	2100–1900
Middle Minoan II	1900–1700
Middle Minoan III	1700–1580
Late Minoan I	1580–1450
Late Minoan II	1450–1400
Late Minoan III	1400–1200

Early Minoan I begins with the arrival in Crete of the settlers from Egypt, and of some non-Egyptian settlers, probably from Asia Minor, who had been influenced by Mesopotamian civilization. Trading relations with Egypt and with the Cyclades began early, and there is evidence that Greece and Troy were reached. The long ships with high prows, like the type depicted in Egypt at an early period, were painted on Minoan pottery.

Copper continued in use for a time, but suddenly bronze was introduced into Crete. It appears to have come from Asia, perhaps by way of Troy, and the Minoans then began to manufacture this amalgam. Before they could do so, however, they had to obtain tin, but it is not certain where the earliest supplies of that rare metal were obtained. The source may have been northern Persia or some area in Asia

Minor. Ultimately supplies were drawn from the west. It is known that there were at one time deposits of tin in western Italy, in Spain, and in north-western France, but the richest tin deposits of Europe were to be found in south-western England. The search for tin must have kept explorers active for a long period. Seafarers of Crete appear to have been engaged in this search. In a burial cave in Etruria in western Italy archæologists have found a typical Early Minoan dagger and two tin buttons. Apparently tin was highly prized by the man in whose tomb these buttons were placed. These may have been his "mascots" for his tin-searching voyages. Etruria became known subsequently as the land of the Etruscans, a people who had connexions with the Ægean area, and with the settlements of easterners in south-western Spain who visited Britain and obtained tin from Cornwall and jet from Whitby in Yorkshire. Perhaps the Etruscans were a mixed people. Overland traders from Central Europe may have met and mingled with seafarers in Etruria and formed the Etruscan nation, which was very powerful when Rome was still a very small city state.

The Minoans of Crete prospered during the four centuries of the Early Minoan II period, which came to a close about 2400 B.C. One or two trading towns in the eastern part of the island, including Palaikastro and Zakro, seem to have been independent. During the three centuries of the Early Minoan III period, however, the influence of Knossos on the northern coast of the central part of the island was growing steadily, as was also that of Phæstos in the south. Rival kings may have reigned at both these centres for a time, but ultimately there was only one ruling family. Palaces were erected at Knossos and Phæstos.

At Knossos clay jars about as big as modern beer casks were manufactured to store olive oil, which was in great demand in Egypt. Standard weights were in use, including the Egyptian shekel, and merchants had button seals made of Egyptian ivory to mark as their personal property the bales of goods which were carried to foreign markets by the Minoan seafarers.

Great progress was made in the arts and crafts in the Middle Minoan I period. The goldsmiths produced fine jewellery, imitating natural objects, and gems were carved with wonderful skill. Potters, having acquired the potter's wheel, were manufacturing beautiful wares which were carried by the Minoan sea-traders to the Cyclades, to Cyprus, to the Syrian coast, and to Egypt. A remarkable find in the ruins of the early palace of Knossos is the statuette of an Egyptian noble which had been shaped in the Nile valley. At the period to which this statuette belongs, Cretan ware of a type called Kamares reached Upper Egypt. Evidently the Minoans and the Egyptians were in close touch. Some think that the rise of the kingship in Crete was due to very intimate Egyptian influence. On the other hand, it may well be that the Minoan governing class at Knossos were merely imitating the Egyptian method of government.

Great changes were meantime taking place in the area which was to become known as Greece. The Achæans, a people of Aryan speech, were moving southward through Thessaly. They were armed with effective bronze weapons, and they changed the simple civilization of the country which they conquered. Intruders reached the Cyclades, but it is not certain whence they came.

The Middle Minoan II period was brought to a close by a

Section of the Frieze in a Minoan Pavilion discovered at Knossos

Hoopoes occur at intervals among red-legged partridges.   Reproduced by permission of Sir Arthur Evans.

disaster in Crete in 1700 B.C. Palaces and other buildings were suddenly wrecked, not only in the centre of the island but also in the eastern towns of Palaikastro, Zakro, &c. Fires broke out, as we know, for at Knossos ashes lie over part of the Middle Minoan II remains. Some of the remains, however, have been discovered under the debris of fallen walls.

Sir Arthur Evans has suggested that a great earthquake had taken place. Fires may have broken out among the ruins of buildings when fallen timber was ignited from the hearths. This explanation seems to be a better one than the theory of an invasion from Asia Minor or from the mainland of the country that was to become known as Greece. It may be, however, that a revolution broke out in Crete after the earthquake took place. This disaster may have been regarded as a sign that the gods were angry with the existing state of affairs.

In the next period—Middle Minoan III—it is found that the power of Crete in the Ægean area not only remained strong but had grown stronger than before. New palaces were built at Knossos and Phæstos, and the other towns were repaired. A new town was founded at Gournia in the Gulf of Mirabello on the north coast of eastern Crete. Knossos became more important than ever, and it may be that the king, who had his seat in the new palace there, ruled over the whole island, and the prince who lived in the palace of Phæstos was subject to him. The power of Knossos spread to southern Greece, where Minoan colonists were settling as traders.

In the Late Minoan I period (1580–1450 B.C.) the Minoan influence in Crete advanced steadily, and Mycenæ, Tyrins, and other towns on the Greek mainland were becoming important centres of commerce. The Minoan seafarers were also carrying on a brisk trade in the western Mediterranean area. There were colonies in Sicily, Sardinia, and southern Spain, and from these enterprising explorers had for long been visiting the north-western coast of Gaul and south-western England. Southern Russia was reached by the merchants who sailed up the Dardanelles and coasted round the Black Sea. The influence of the Minoans also reached central Europe.

It is customary to refer to the Late Minoan II period, which lasted for about half a century (1450–1400 B.C.), as the "Golden Age of Crete". Knossos had become the chief centre of commerce on the island, and the towns of Gournia, Palaikastro, and Zakro shrank in importance. The Minos kings (perhaps Minos was a royal title) were supreme, and the rulers of Mycenæ, Tyrins, Thebes, Corinth, and Athens were their vassals. During the Late Minoan I period Egypt had made great conquests in western Asia, and the Minoan king at Knossos sent presents to the Pharaoh Thothmes III, "the Napoleon of Egypt". Apparently Crete had benefited greatly by the peace which the Egyptians were able to establish in western Asia.

Thucydides, the Greek historian, who was born about 471 B.C., heard traditions about the King of Crete, who was remembered as Minos, and wrote:

"The first person known to us by tradition as having established a navy is Minos. He made himself master of what is now called the Hellenic Sea, and ruled over the Cyclades, into most of which he sent the first colonists, expelling the Carians and appointing his own sons governors; and thus did his best to put down piracy in those waters, a necessary step to secure revenues for his own use. For in early times the Hellenes (Greeks) and the barbarians of the coast and islands, as communication by sea became more common, were tempted to turn pirates, under the leadership of their most powerful men; the motives being to get wealth for themselves and to support their poor. They would fall upon a town unprotected by walls, and consisting of a mere collection of villages, and would plunder it. Indeed this came to be the main source of their livelihood, no disgrace being yet attached to such an achievement, but even some glory.

"An illustration of this is furnished by the honour with which some of the inhabitants of the continent still regard a successful marauder, and by the question we find the old poets making the people ask of the seafarers, 'Are you pirates?' It seems as if those who were asked such a question were not ashamed to confess they were and that the questioners did not reproach them for being pirates. The same system of robbery was common on land also."

The historian tells that the ancient inhabitants of Greece used to find it necessary to carry weapons to protect themselves and their homes against sea and land robbers. Towns had to be built at some distance from the sea and to be protected by walls. After Minos built his navy "communication by sea became safer", the historian tells us:

"The coast populations began to apply themselves more closely to the acquisition of wealth, and their life became more settled; some began to build strong walls to protect their property. The love of gain reconciled the weaker to the government of the stronger, while the possession of capital made it possible for the powerful cities to reduce the smaller ones to subjection."

The Cretan towns were not fortified like those on the Greek mainland. Minos depended for the defence of his country upon his "wooden walls", that is, his navy; but a time came when his rivals suddenly crossed the sea from the coast of southern Greece and landed a strong army in Crete, which overthrew the Minoan power. According to tradition Minos had gone to Sicily with his fleet to make conquests there when undefended Crete was attacked by his powerful rivals.

The palaces of Knossos and Phæstos were taken and set on fire, while the towns of Gournia, Pseira, Zakro, and Palaikastro were sacked and given to the flames. A new government was set up, but Crete was after that time simply a subject state, for the supremacy had passed to Mycenæ and Tyrins and other city states on the mainland. Many Minoan refugees fled across the sea and settled in Cyprus, Asia Minor, and Syria; others found new homes on the islands in the west.

CHAPTER XIX

Colonies of Farmers and Sailors

A new era dawned in western Europe when the last land movement was taking place and the country we know as Britain was finally separated from the continent. The archæologists have called it the Neolithic (new stone) Age because certain tools were polished and were given sharp edges by being rubbed on grindstones. Not only was flint treated in this way but also other very hard stones.

Flint arrow-heads were still chipped, but with much greater skill than were Azilian flints, and they were given a variety of forms which recalled those of earlier times, some imitating the horn harpoons by being barbed, others the older leaf-shaped and triangular lance-points, while some forms were quite new.

The polished stone axe or adze was a wonderful invention. When a genuine one is laid on its side it is found to be so perfectly balanced that it revolves on a centre of gravity. It was, no doubt, sharpened on a grindstone, but it must first have been carefully measured, and then polished with the aid of emery or sand.

This kind of stone axe or adze proved to be very useful and continued in use long after metal tools were invented. Indeed, it is only in our own day that the stone axe has begun finally to disappear. In Polynesia, into which area it was introduced by seafarers, boat-builders did excellent and delicate work with it in quite recent times. An American writer tells that he saw a Polynesian workman using a polished stone adze with great skill, and says:

"In watching the shaping of a canoe I have seen the old canoe-maker use for the rough shaping and excavating an ordinary foreign steel adze; but for the finishing touches he dropped the foreign tool and returned to the adze of his ancestors, and the blunt-looking stone cut off a delicate shaving from the very hard *Koa* wood, and never seemed to take too much wood, as the foreign adze was apt to do. That skill was an important element in the use, I was convinced, for with all the teaching of the native I could only make a dent where I tried to raise a shaving."

When the term "Neolithic Age" is applied to a period of history in western Europe, it refers to much more than the new method of working stone. A very definite era of progress had set in during this age. Agriculture was introduced, herds and flocks of domesticated animals were kept, fruit-trees were cultivated. Flax was grown so that linen might be made from it, wool was used to make clothing by knitting and weaving, and pottery was manufactured.

Of great importance, too, is the fact that boats came into use in western Europe in the Neolithic Age.

Some archæologists have drawn attention of late to the interesting fact that Neolithic culture in Europe was, to begin with, mainly coastal—that is, it crept along the shores of the Mediterranean before it penetrated into central Europe. The seeds of cultivated barley, wheat, &c., were evidently carried by ancient mariners to the lands occupied by Azilian and other fishermen and hunters.

The natives among whom the newcomers settled did not necessarily change at once their ancient habits of life. Some time must have elapsed before agricultural civilization was adopted. Its benefits would have been appreciated first during a period of scarcity, when, owing to cold and stormy weather, animals became scarce and fish difficult to obtain. The food producers would then be able to give hospitality to hungry hunters and their families. When the strangers had acquired knowledge of the language of the natives and were able to converse with them, a beginning would be made in giving them instruction and help in return for services rendered. The natives had, of course, to obtain supplies of seed, but it was absolutely necessary that they should also acquire knowledge of the agricultural calendar if they were to conduct farming operations with success. They had therefore to be taught to study the movements of the heavenly bodies. In this connexion it is of interest to find that in primitive agricultural communities farming operations are timed by the rising of certain stars or the seasonal aspect of groups of stars. The "clock" of the seasons in ancient Europe was the constellation of *Ursa Major* ("The Great Bear"), which in our agricultural folk-lore has been remembered by such significant names as "The Plough" and "Charles's Wain". It will be observed that when this group of stars becomes visible as night comes on, the "tail" or "handle" is directed eastward in spring, southward in summer, westward in autumn, and northward in winter. Sowing time is indicated in our own land when the "handle" of "The Plough" points towards the east. The month is measured by the moon, and we have not yet forgotten the "Harvest moon", while the ancient belief that the moon exercises a beneficial influence upon crops is still widely remembered. In Gaelic folk-lore we also detect an interest in the sun. The year was divided into two parts—the period of the "big sun" of summer and the period of the "little sun" of winter. Each of these periods was subdivided, and the year had therefore four quarters. Ceremonies were performed at the beginning of each quarter to ensure health, wealth, and prosperity—that is, "luck". Bonfires were lit and men and cattle were supposed to receive protection by passing through the smoke or over the embers. It was possible, too, according to folk-belief, to peer into the future on the night preceding a quarter day. Hence the divination ceremonies connected with Hallowe'en, New Year's Day, Beltane (1st May), and Midsummer's Night. According to Gaelic folk-belief, each quarter was critical, for the fairies, giants, and other supernatural beings then broke loose, and human beings had to protect themselves by reciting charms, hanging certain plants round their dwellings—the Christmas decoration of houses had origin in this custom—and by performing protective ceremonies. The introduction of the agricultural calendar thus entailed the introduction of the magico-religious ideas and practices, and also the myths connected with the agricultural mode of life.

Every phase of agricultural life is found to have a heritage of immemorial superstitious practices. When, for instance, a field had been tilled, the sowing was performed by an elderly man. If he should be interrupted, some misfortune was sure to happen. The sower was possessed of charms which aided him in his work. A Gaelic folk-story tells that one day an elderly Hebridean, who carried seed oats in a sheet suspended from his shoulders like a plaid, was engaged in sowing, when a man, observing that the supply of seed did not seem to diminish, uttered a magical exclamation and asked if the sheet would never be emptied. Immediately a small fairy bird flew out of the sheet and the supply of seed was soon exhausted, part of the field remaining unsown. The spell had been broken!

In agricultural folk-lore we find fragments of myths that could not possibly have had origin in this country and may have been imported with the agricultural mode of life. A Scottish folk-tale, for instance, describes an underworld paradise in which the dead are seen reaping corn in fields watered by numerous small streams. We have here, apparently, a memory of the paradise of Osiris, the streams being the irrigation channels of Egypt.

A Gaelic story explains why a famous seer was called "Son of the dead woman". His father had been slain and dismembered by an enemy, and the widow engaged a tailor to sew the body together before burial. After she herself died, her ghost appeared to the tailor, requesting him to open her grave. He did so and found in it a newly-born child whom he fostered. This seems like a version of the myth of Set slaying Osiris and the posthumous birth of Horus.

The earliest centre of Neolithic culture in Europe was the island of Crete. Cretan and other seafarers sailed westward towards Sicily and Italy and ultimately to Spain; and we have already seen that some daring explorers navigated their boats as far north as the River Clyde in south-western Scotland.

It is not possible to date the beginnings of Neolithic civilization in the various parts of Europe in which it was established.

Once the new quickening influence from the east made the hunters and fishermen in a particular area adopt new habits of life, progress set in and local development took place. Local inventors introduced new forms of tools, and made new use of the tools they had acquired from colonists.

People who lived on islands had often to put to sea to obtain materials which they required, and these improved their boats and became better navigators. Those peoples who lived in inland valleys were more concerned about other things than boat-building. Some erected lake dwellings by cutting down trees and erecting the houses on " stilts ", so as to be safe from the attacks of beasts of prey and human robbers.

There were " lake dwellers " in Switzerland and their relics show how their civilization was developed. The earliest had stone axes or adzes made from local rock. They also used bone tools and they made pottery. Then larger stone axes or adzes came into use, and some of these were made from rock not found in Switzerland. Apparently the improved stone tool was introduced by new settlers. The third phase shows improved stone-working as a result of local development; but as metal was coming into use, it is possible that the late quickening influence resulted from the arrival of new peoples.

In Crete the artisans made sharp knives from obsidian—a natural glass from hardened lava. The obsidian was imported by mariners from the island of Melos in the Cyclades (the islands sprinkled over the Ægean sea). From Naxos they obtained emery, and it was used for making stone bowls by grinding them into shape and hollowing them out with the aid of drills. Emery was also introduced into Egypt and used there by the workmen who made small and large stone vessels.

The seafarers who settled in Malta imported jade and

jadeite to make little axe-head amulets as occasionally did the pre-dynastic Egyptians.

In ancient as in modern times, the seafarers searched for and traded in articles that may be referred to as luxuries. Some of these were used for superstitious reasons. They believed that if certain things were worn as ornaments, the life of the wearers would be prolonged. They were thus supposed to be "lucky" as mascots, protecting individuals against accidents, bringing them "good fortune" and so on.

One substance which came into fashion as a "luck bringer" was amber. Experts have examined the amber ornaments discovered in some ancient sites in southern Europe and find that a good deal of it came from the Baltic. The demand for lucky amber must have made the early people go on long voyages or undertake long journeys. An important result of the traffic in amber was the diffusion of civilization in the areas visited by the traders.

The Neolithic era of progress was introduced into the country we now know as England by seafarers. The islands known as Britain and Ireland then were very thinly peopled by hunters and fishermen. After the seafarers began to arrive, however, the seeds of barley, wheat, &c., and of certain fruit-trees were introduced, as were also domesticated animals. Then little communities were formed in localities suitable for farming and gardening.

The Neolithic civilization spread gradually throughout Britain, but although in some districts the Neolithic implements came into fashion, the people were chiefly hunters and fishermen all the year round. They thus continued to be "food gatherers", although they owed much to the agriculturists who were "food producers". It is possible that it was from the seafarers who introduced the elements of Neolithic civilization that the hunters learned how to preserve flesh by salting it.

In some of the old Celtic folk-stories we find memories of the life led by people who were chiefly hunters. A Gaelic tale tells of a band of ancient hunters on the island of Skye. During the winter they lived in a cave, their chief food being shell-fish and milk. One day a hunter called "Thinman", who was a swift runner, was "sent out to look for deer". The others "gathered limpets at Loch Snizort". "When he (Thinman) saw the game, he gave a shout which was heard by the rest . . . who were at the time eating shell-fish at Loch Snizort." They at once left "the unsavoury food" and "set off to where the chase was to be found".

Another old Gaelic story tells that during a long hard winter the hunters lived in small houses surrounded by a stockade. There were no signs of deer, and food was therefore very scarce. The women, however, "still kept their good looks, while the men were becoming meagre and ill-looking". It was found, the story tells, that the women were getting nourishment from the "leaves of trees, the roots of heather, and tops of hazels". Another version of the tale tells that the women ate "the roots of ferns".

A curious old Gaelic story is about a hunter who had "the right to marrow bones". He was called "Goll" because he was squint-eyed. Goll kept the largest of the marrow bones for his mother. She "was aged, and had lost her teeth", and "she lived on the marrow".

In certain stories we find that some of the hunters had spears of hard wood. They were accustomed to make these sharp by thrusting them into a fire and then rubbing them on rock.

CHAPTER XX

The Discovery of Metals

The discovery of metals was one of very great importance in the history of early man. Antiquaries are not agreed where this discovery was first made. Some favour Egypt, some Asia Minor, and some an area in south-western Persia which was anciently known as Elam.

The metals first used were gold and copper and iron. Now, Egypt was the country which in ancient times was famous for its gold. It was found chiefly in the Eastern Desert between Upper Egypt and the Red Sea. A writer on the subject tells us:

"Prospectors in the Eastern Desert report that immense alluvial workings are encountered, especially in the Wadi Allagi, where the hills, as a result, have the appearance of having been ploughed. Quite 100 square miles of country has been worked to an average depth of seven feet. So thoroughly has this been done that only the merest traces of gold remain."

A wadi is a dry water-course, which was formed when Egypt was a wetter country than it is in our day. At the time when Europe was partly covered with ice, torrents poured down from the Eastern Desert into the great lake which lay between the cliffs of Egypt.

The ancient Egyptians found veins of gold in quartz in some of the wadis, while nuggets of gold and gold-dust were washed from the old torrent beds of gravel and sand.

In some part of the Eastern Desert small "pockets" of gold are still found. After one of those rare showers of rain, which fall perhaps once in three years in the Eastern Desert, the gold-dust can be seen glittering in the moonlight, having been "washed" out by the pelting rain. Perhaps the earliest workers in metal learned how to "wash" gold from the sand after seeing the rain doing it.

Gold is a soft metal and useless for making tools. The Egyptians used it, as other peoples used amber, to make lucky ornaments or amulets. Some of the oldest gold ornaments were models of whorled snail-shells. Snail-shells and sea-shells were worn in Egypt at a very early period as they were by the Cro-Magnons in western Europe. The handles of some ancient Egyptian flint knives were covered with or made of gold, as has been already stated.

The people who lived in Egypt before the historical period not only used gold for lucky ornaments but also pieces of the beautiful green stone called malachite. Now, malachite is an ore of copper. It is found in some of the wadis and among the hills of the Eastern Desert. When malachite is placed in a fire, copper runs out of it. Perhaps copper was first discovered by accident, a piece of malachite having fallen into a fire.

In some of the pre-dynastic graves of Egypt the archæologists have found copper needles with one end bent so as to form what has been called the "hook-eye". Pins of copper were used also. These and copper beads and copper bracelets were worn long before any cutting-tools of copper had been invented. The first copper tools were chisels, which were invented during the latter part of the pre-dynastic age.

Iron was used in pre-dynastic Egypt, as was gold, as a luck-bringing or sacred metal. Beads of hammered iron have been found in some pre-dynastic graves. One necklace had iron beads strung alternately with gold beads.

The earliest known Egyptian text referring to iron belongs

to the age when the pyramids were being erected as tombs for the pharaohs. Iron is called "Metal of the Sky". The Egyptians believed that the sky was made of iron, but whether they did so because they discovered that ærolites (iron meteors) fall from the sky, or because they had connected iron as a sacred metal with a deity of the sky, is uncertain. After iron beads went out of fashion, little pieces of hammered iron were, during the early dynasties, used as "lucky objects", but no iron weapons were known in Egypt before 1200 B.C.

Egyptian Crank Drill invented in the early Dynastic Period (about 3400–3000 B.C.)

(After Borchardt.)

An important invention was made in Egypt some time before 3000 B.C. This was the crank drill, which was used for drilling out stone vessels. Below the handle two stone weights were suspended, and these served the same purpose as does a modern fly-wheel; they kept the shaft revolving. The point of the shaft was forked so as to hold a "cutter". At first the cutter was a hard and sharp stone. Then a copper cutter was introduced.

With this invention of the crank-driven shaft the "Age of Machinery" began. As Professor Breasted emphasizes, the revolving machine "involved the essential principle of the wheel with a vertical axis". The wheel "as a burden-bearing device with a horizontal axis" was not, however, invented in

Egypt, but, so far as we know, in Mesopotamia. The Egyptians used round logs by placing them under blocks of stone which were hauled from the quarries, but they did not invent the wheeled cart. The potter's wheel was in use in Elam (western Persia) at an early period, and, as some think, before it was in use in Egypt.

For many centuries after copper was utilized in Egypt for making chisels, drill-cutters, &c., flint knives, flint arrowheads, &c., were still being made. Indeed, stone tools continued in use in Egypt till about 2000 B.C. Not a few archæologists are of opinion that polished stone axes or adzes were invented after the introduction of copper tools. These stone axes are a feature of the Neolithic Age in western Europe.

Egypt, therefore, passed from its Palæolithic Age to its Copper Age, during which gold and iron were worked, before its Neolithic industry was developed.

Bronze was introduced into Egypt long after it had been known in Crete and in western Asia. The invention of bronze, which is an amalgam of copper and tin, took place somewhere in northern Mesopotamia or northern Persia. It was possibly the Sumerian colonists who, about 3000 B.C., discovered that soft Asiatic copper could be hardened by mixing it with a small proportion of tin. The copper found and used by the Egyptians was naturally hard.

It was not until about 2000 B.C. that bronze daggers and razors were becoming common in Egypt. Swords of bronze and bronze battle-axes were being adopted, but copper weapons continued in use. The general adoption of bronze came later.

In western and central Europe the order of the archæological ages was (1) the Palæolithic, (2) the Neolithic, (3) the Bronze, and (4) the Iron. There is no trace of iron having been used in Europe before bronze was introduced.

The European Neolithic industry appears to have been introduced by intruders who had adopted the agricultural mode of life and in some areas searched for and used gold. In southern Spain the early users of Neolithic tools gathered

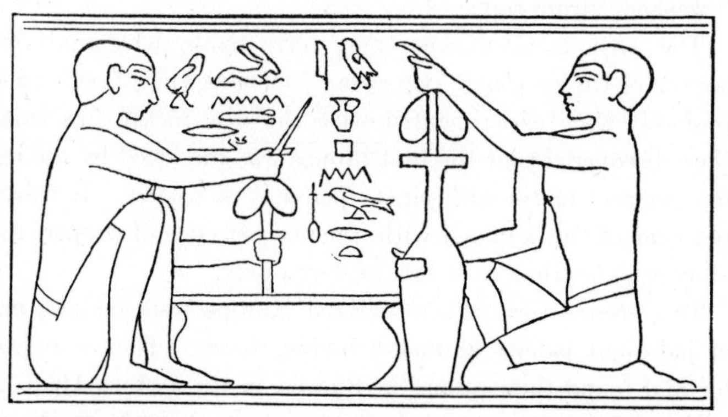

Egyptian Craftsmen engaged in Drilling out Stone Vessels with the Crank Drill

The hieroglyphs record the workmen's conversation. One says: "This is a very beautiful vase". The other replies: "It is indeed". From a tomb relief (after De Morgan).

copper ores and exported them. Perhaps these were seafaring colonists from the east. In their own countries copper had long been in use, but they themselves used Neolithic tools. The early miners broke up gold-bearing quartz and copper ores with stone hammers. They did not always require metal tools for their work. Neolithic tools served them well in their activities as miners, agriculturists, and seafarers. Fint arrows and stone hammers continued in use in central and western Europe long after bronze was introduced. Metal tools were adopted very gradually. Ores were scarce and had to be searched for far and near.

Bronze was introduced into Europe from western Asia. The metal-workers in that area are believed to have discovered tin at Khorassan in north-eastern Persia, and perhaps somewhere in Asia Minor too. Tin crystals are found in rocks and "stream-tin" in sand, and stream-tin, like gold-dust, can be "washed" from soil.

The early metal-workers may have made accidental discovery of tin by using "tin-stone" to bank their fires. Then probably they experimented with the new metal. In time, they discovered that the best bronze was produced by mixing ten per cent of tin with ninety per cent of copper. If thirty per cent of tin is mixed with seventy per cent of copper, the alloy is so brittle that it breaks very easily.

The bronze-carriers who entered Europe were making use of jade and jadeite as luck-bringing stones. They searched for and found these stones in Europe, in the eastern Alps. A variety of jadeite was worked near Maurach in Switzerland. Jadeite was found also at Mount Viso in Italy, while boulders of jade were discovered in Germany and layers of it in the Zobten mountains in Silesia. Jade pebbles have been picked up in the Western Isles of Scotland. In beds of tin a green stone, called "callais", is occasionally found. It resembles jade, but is really a variety of turquoise. Polished axe amulets were made of callais by the early metal-workers in Europe. It is unlikely, however, that jade, jadeite, and callais would have been searched for unless the metal-workers had, before entering Europe, regarded these hard coloured stones with superstitious reverence.

Search was made also for copper and tin. In time tin was

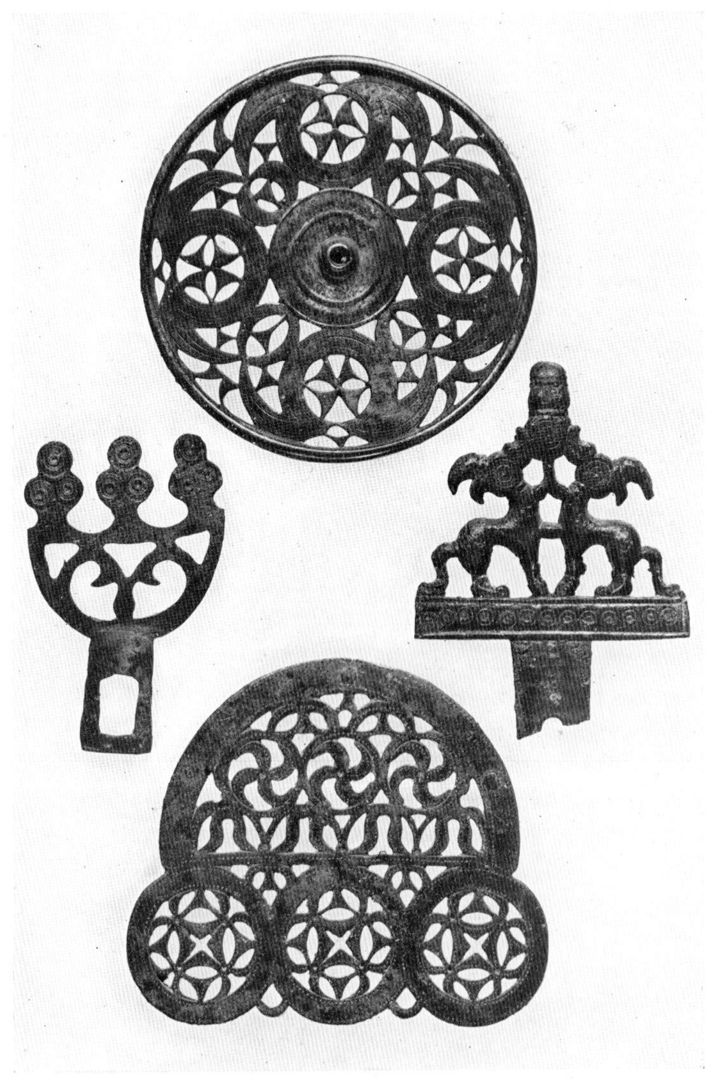

BRONZE-WORK FROM CHARIOT-BURIAL,
SOMME BIONNE, MARNE, FRANCE

By permission of the Trustees of the British Museum. See page 150

found in considerable quantities in Devon and Cornwall. At first it was picked up on the surface of the ground. Tin-mines were subsequently opened in Cornwall. Traces of tin have been located in the Scilly Isles, in Finland, in the province of Auvergne in central France, in Brittany, in Saxony, in western Spain, and in Morocco. There are Gaelic place-names in Scotland in which the name for tin occurs. Tin and copper are found together in Indo-China and China, as in Cornwall. Copper was found in South Wales, in north-western England, and in parts of Scotland. An ancient copper-mine was recently reopened in Shetland. Lead, which was scarce in ancient times, could be discovered in England, in south-eastern Scotland, chiefly at Linlithgow, and in the Orkneys.

In the south of Spain and Portugal traces have been discovered of colonists who were in touch with the old civilizations of Egypt and Mesopotamia. From their graves have been collected objects made of hippopotamus ivory from Egypt, beads made from African ostrich eggs, alabaster cups, painted vases, little idols very like those found in Crete, Troy, and Mesopotamia, &c. In one grave was discovered a gold coronet from Egypt and in another a shell from the Red Sea.

These colonists were seafarers, and must be distinguished from the carriers of bronze who entered Europe from western Asia and penetrated to central Europe. They sailed northward round the coasts of modern Spain, Portugal, and France, and reached the Baltic and the British Isles. Among their relics are objects of amber from the Baltic and jet from Whitby in Yorkshire. Reference has already been made to the greenstone axe found in one of the ancient Glasgow boats. Similar axes of greenstone have been unearthed among the remains of the ancient colonies of easterners in Spain.

The oldest forms of bronze tools and weapons come from western Asia. When bronze was introduced into Europe new forms were being adopted. The oldest Chinese bronzes are not of the earliest known types. The bronze axes and bronze sickles first used by the Mongols in the Chinese area are similar to those which were introduced into Europe.

During the Bronze Age, which began at different periods in different areas, there were widespread movements of races in Europe and Asia. When the searchers for metals founded colonies, backward peoples adopted the new civilization and developed it to suit local needs. New centres of civilization thus came into existence, and from these explorers and other adventurers went forth and they reached and peopled out-lying areas.

On the island of Crete the great Minoan civilization began after copper had come into use. Then bronze was introduced, apparently from western Asia, and the Cretan Bronze Age continued until after the fall of the Minoan power. About 1200 B.C. iron was suddenly introduced into Crete from the Greek mainland by intruders who overran and conquered the island. These intruders had previously overrun the country which was to become known as Greece. They came from the north, probably from Asia Minor, and after settling in the Danube valley and mixing with the people there, they set out with their iron weapons to conquer ancient states in which bronze weapons were still in use.

Iron, as we have seen, was known and utilized at a very remote period in Egypt, but only as a "luck" metal. This superstitious iron connexion still survives in some areas where the expression "touch iron" may still be heard. Iron was supposed to protect one against fairies, witches, and other "enemies of man".

The Iron Age of the archæologists does not begin, however, until iron began to supplant bronze for tools and weapons. Between 1300 and 1200 B.C. iron was used in Mesopotamia. The Hittites of Asia Minor worked iron-mines in the thirteenth century B.C. In northern Mesopotamia the Assyrians adopted iron weapons and iron armour, and their armies used the new weapons with terrible effect, making extensive conquests. A quantity of buried iron ingots has been unearthed in the ruins of the ancient Assyrian city of Nineveh, which lies opposite modern Mosul. The ingots were shaped like shuttles and were of various sizes, weighing from about nine pounds to forty-four pounds each. Each ingot was perforated at one end, as if to be strung so as to be easily carried by men and animals. Probably the supplies of iron required by the Assyrian blacksmiths were transported from the iron-mines of north-eastern Asia.

The Iron Age of Greece began after 1200 B.C. and the Cretan Iron Age before 1100 B.C. In the Ægean area the Iron Age is also called the "Homeric Age", because the warriors, whose exploits are celebrated in the epics of the Greek poet Homer, used weapons of iron as well as armour of bronze.

From the Danube area the use of iron passed into central Europe and into Italy, where the beginning of the Iron Age is usually dated about 1000 B.C.

In western Europe the working of iron was highly developed and improved and the earliest known steel was introduced. According to a Greek writer, the Romans adopted the swords made by the Iberians of Spain. He says, however, that although the Romans imitated the shapes of Iberian swords, they could not manufacture such good steel.

CHAPTER XXI

The Civilization of the Charioteers

When Julius Cæsar wrote an account of his two expeditions to Britain, which were made in 55 B.C. and 54 B.C., he told that the inhabitants were numerous, that the houses were similar to those of Gaul, and that the people in the south had farms and flocks and herds. Chariots were used in battle, and the drivers were so well trained that they could pull up or turn their horses at a moment's notice, and run out along the chariot pole to stand astride the yoke, and then return quickly with astonishing dexterity.

A still earlier visitor was Pytheas, the Greek explorer, who sailed from Marseilles to Britain about the year 330 B.C. He wrote an account of his voyage, but it has not survived except in fragments, which are found quoted in the works of later writers. He sailed along the east coast as far north as Orkney, crossed the North Sea to Scandinavia, and returned to Britain again. According to Strabo, a Greek writer, who was born about 50 B.C., Pytheas saw farms in Britain. Instead of using open-air threshing floors, such as were known in southern Europe, the British farmers carried their corn-ears into barns and threshed them there. They had many domesticated animals. In the Hebrides the people did not till the land but lived solely on fish and milk. Apparently coal was used in some parts of Britain. Pytheas told that in a temple of a goddess the fires never went out, yet never whitened into ashes. "When," he related, "the fire has got dull, it turns into round lumps like stones."

In the northern parts of Britain, Pytheas found that the nights were bright and very short. The interval between sunset and sunrise was scarcely perceptible.

Pytheas appears to have visited Britain to obtain information regarding its trade for the Greek merchants at Marseilles. The Phœnicians of Carthage and Cadiz in Spain kept secret the route to the islands which yielded tin and were known vaguely as the Cassiterides. The Greek name for tin was "cassiteros", and S. Reinach, the French scholar, suggests that it was so called after the "Cassi", a Celtic people, who were engaged in the tin trade, and he cites the Celtic tribal names of Cassi-mara, Bodio-casses, Vidu-casses, &c.

In the *Iliad*, one of the two great epics of the Greek poet, Homer, who lived about 900 B.C., tin is called *cassiteros*. The poet may have heard about the wonderful land of Britain, where the summer nights were so short, for in his other epic, the *Odyssey* (Book X), there is an account of an island called Lamos where "double wages might be earned by a sleepless man, one wage as a cowherd and one as a shepherd of white flocks, because the out-goings of the night and the day are so very near".

Poseidonius, a Greek writer who visited Britain, found it was "thickly populated", and he saw many farms. "A number of kings and chiefs govern the country," he wrote, "and these, as a rule, live in peace with one another." In Cornwall the people were friendly to strangers. They worked the mines there, and conveyed tin in great quantities in their wagons to an island called Ictis, which could be reached at low tide. There it was purchased by merchants who transported it to Gaul (France), across which country it was carried by horses to the Mediterranean coast. Poseidonius also stated that in war the Britons used chariots. When Scotland was invaded by the Romans under Agricola, the Caledonians also used chariots in battle.

Chariots came originally from Asia. They were used by the warriors whose battles are described in the *Iliad* of Homer, and they were introduced into central and western Europe during the archæological Iron Age (900–100 B.C.). The first period of the Iron Age is known as the Hallstatt period, after Hallstatt in Austria. Hallstatt culture reached as far west as Spain and Portugal, but touched Britain only very slightly. It was during the second phase of this culture, which is dated from about 700 B.C. till 500 B.C., that chariots were laid in the tombs of Continental warriors. Greek objects have been found in some of the graves of the Hallstatt period in central Europe and in Italy. Bronze continued in use for a variety of purposes, but iron was favoured for weapons. Gold was used to make articles for personal wear, such as ear-rings, arm-rings, &c., and for religious purposes, as is suggested by a beautiful gold bowl with symbolic designs which belongs to the Late Hallstatt period, and was found near Zurich in Switzerland.

The next period of the Iron Age is known as the La Tène period. On the Continent it is dated from 500 B.C. till 100 B.C. or later. The culture of La Tène survived in Britain till the period of the Roman occupation. The name of this culture is derived from a typical site at La Tène, at the eastern end of Lake Neuchâtel in Switzerland. There, among the interesting discoveries which throw light on the customs of the people of the period, were wooden yokes for horses and oxen, parts of pack saddles, fish hooks, barbed tridents for weapons and for spearing fish, boat hooks, and boar spears. Evidently at La Tène the agricultural mode of life was practised, horses were used by traders, fish were caught and wild animals were hunted. Dug-out canoes were favoured by fishermen. Warriors used chariots and also rode on horseback. Swords were of iron, and were made sharp by hammering their edges; their scabbards were of iron with bronze ornamentation, and many of these were engraved with animal and symbolic designs. Spears and javelins were common, but barbed-iron arrows were rare.

The chief warriors wore helmets of bronze. Some of these, including a fine example found in the Thames, London, were of horned design like the horned helmets of Mesopotamia, Greece, and Italy. Two types of shield were in use. At first the semi-cylindrical shield was favoured; then one of the 8-form variety became general. A magnificent specimen, developed from the latter type, was found in the Thames at Battersea and is known as the "Battersea Shield". It is of bronze and beautifully designed and ornamented with symbolic designs exquisitely used by the artist. In the red enamel "studs" are swastikas which were widely used in ancient times as symbols of divinity, and were probably supposed to have a protective value. Another symbol favoured was the wild boar. Tacitus, the Roman historian (*Germania*, Chap. XLV), tells us that the Baltic amber-traders regarded the boar as a religious symbol, and believed that the warriors who wore boar-amulets were protected by them in battle. Coral, which was imported from the Mediterranean, was used also as a protective agency, and weapons, helmets, and shields were adorned with it. Red enamel was a substitute for coral, and other precious substances were imitated in white, blue, and yellow enamels, so as to adorn amulets, chariot ornaments of symbolic design, bits of horses, mirrors, &c. The enamels of the ancient Britons in England, Scotland, and Ireland are the finest ever manufactured by any craftsmen in the world. It is evident that there were highly-skilled artisans and decorative artists in Britain prior to the Roman occupation. Metal-working had reached a high state of excellence. It is a mistake to imagine that the ancient Britons were merely half savage and treacherous people, " running wild in the woods ", until Roman civilization was introduced. The influences of the ancient Oriental civilizations had reached Britain before Rome was built. In ancient graves in south-western England have been found, for instance, blue beads of Egyptian manufacture which were imported as far back as the time of Tut-ankh-amon. Probably they came by sea. These beads were subsequently imitated by local craftsmen in England, Scotland, and Ireland. They are of a glassy character, having been manufactured by mixing copper and sandstone. It would appear, therefore, that not only were Oriental beads introduced into Britain, but also the knowledge of how to manufacture them, and the magico-religious beliefs which caused them to be worn as were protective coral-amulets and boar-amulets (or mascots). They were, in short, " luck beads ". The habit of wearing certain things for " luck " has not entirely died out even in our own day. We still have amulets and mascots.

The battle-chariot was no longer used in Gaul (France) when Julius Cæsar conquered that country. The Roman soldiers were therefore greatly alarmed, as Cæsar tells, when they first came into conflict with the British charioteers. They had not been accustomed to this " arm " of warfare. When Agricola invaded Scotland, the Caledonians had chariots, and

GAULISH CHARIOT-BURIAL, SOMME BIONNE, MARNE, FRANCE

From M. Morel's Album, by permission of the Trustees of the British Museum

there is evidence that chariots were common in Ireland also. Roads were necessary in those countries in which chariots and other wheeled vehicles were in use. Pre-Roman roads have been traced in England and Ireland, and in Scotland there are Gaelic place-names which indicate that there were ancient roads through certain mountain passes. After chariots ceased to be used, the old roads became " pony tracks ".

Tacitus tells us in his *Life of Agricola* (Chap. XXIV) that in his day the harbours of Ireland were known to traders, and the manners and customs of the Irish people differed little from those of the ancient Britons. There are ancient Irish-Gaelic manuscripts dating back to the seventh century of the Christian era which refer to events in the first century and earlier. Later manuscripts contain retellings of the ancient oral hero-tales, the obsolete words being supplanted.

The chief tales deal with a war waged against the " Red Branch " warriors of Ulster by the other provinces of Ireland. Vivid descriptions are given of the combatants. In Connaught a force of 3000 fighting men was mustered, and it is told that they were in various " troops ".

One troop had close-shorn, dark hair, and the men wore green mantles and many-coloured cloaks with silver brooches; their swords had silver-adorned hilts, and they had also spears and long shields.

Another troop had their hair cut short in front and left long at the back. They had white linen tunics with red ornamentation which came down to their knees, and above these dark-blue cloaks. Their swords had gold-covered hilts and silver fist-guards, their spears had five prongs, and they carried " shining shields ".

Another troop was made up of fair-yellow and golden-haired men, the hair being short in front and falling behind down to their shoulders. Their cloaks were of purple-red and finely adorned, and these were clasped with brooches of gold; their shields were curved and had sharp edges; their spears were of great length. Apparently this troop was well disciplined, for it is told that "together they raised their feet, and together they set them down again".

The chief hero of the Ulster army was Cuchulain, and it is told that he wore in battle a jacket of "tough, tanned, stout leather", which served "to keep off spears and points and irons and lances and arrows". He had also a "tough, well-sewn kilt of brown leather" which he wore over "silken trews". He had several weapons, including a five-pronged spear, and swords and javelins. A crested helmet protected his head, and on it were four "carbuncle gems". His chariot, which was driven by a red-haired man named Laeg, had iron wheels, and from it protruded scythe-like blades, spikes and prongs, while there were "stinging nails" on the poles. When Cuchulain rode against the foot-soldiers of the enemy he "mowed" them down and left "walls of corpses". In one attack he killed many "without having his blood drawn or wound brought to himself or his charioteer or either of his two horses".

The ancient Gaelic stories are of value in so far as they throw light on the manners and customs and the social organization of the Celtic peoples before the period of written history. It is found that there were among the Celts five classes of people. These were (1) the kings who governed in various districts as vassals of the "High King", (2) the aristocrats who owned land, (3) the Freemen who had property, (4) the Freemen who had no property, and (5) the men who were not free, including serfs and slaves. The higher classes were the Celts, and the lower classes were mainly the descendants of the pre-Celtic peoples who had been subjected by the invading Celts.

The Celts of the Continent were farmers and stock-keepers. They reared horses, cows, sheep, and pigs. According to Roman writers they exported great quantities of salted and smoked bacon to Italy. It is of interest therefore to find that during the Iron Age there were many settlements in salt-yielding areas. The finds at Hallstatt in Austria, which are typical of early Iron Age culture, were made near ancient salt-mines. Hallstatt relics have been discovered in different parts of France near deposits of salt. Archæologists have found evidence that there were Hallstatt salt factories, and that these were conducted on commercial lines. It may be that the culture we know by the name of Hallstatt had its basis in the wealth accumulated by the bacon industry which appears to have been of great economic importance in ancient times.

Commercial contact with south-eastern Europe is reflected in the pottery of the Hallstatt and La Tène cultures. Painted vessels of hand-made pottery of the early La Tène period in France reveal Ægean influence. The potter's wheel was introduced into central and western Europe during the last phase of La Tène culture, and it ultimately reached Britain. Specimens of wheel-turned pottery have been found in ancient Iron Age graves in England. Graves in which chariots have been placed have also been discovered.

During the La Tène phases of Iron Age culture large numbers of Celts appear to have invaded Britain and formed military aristocracies. They used chariots in battle and these remained in use long after they had been superseded by cavalry in Celtic areas on the Continent.

The chariots went out of use in England after the Roman conquest, but, as has been indicated, the Caledonians were using them when Agricola waged his campaigns in Scotland. In the Irish manuscript tales there are references not only to chariot fighting, but to chariot racing at the games which were held on festive occasions. Chariots were, however, possessed by the kings and the nobles alone. One type had two wheels and another four wheels. The latter were used for travelling as well as fighting, and kings and queens rode in chariots which had coloured hoods adorned with the plumage of birds. The value of an ordinary chariot in Ireland was about twelve cows, but a royal chariot was worth about eighty or ninety cows. The driver was a man of high rank, next in importance to the warrior, and he was called the "ara", a name which survives till our own day in the surname MacAra.

Horsed chariots remained in use in Ireland till about the ninth century.

CHAPTER XXII

The Ancient Standing Stones

The most impressive works of ancient man in these islands, and in various parts of the Continent, are the "Standing Stones" or Megaliths. The word megalith means "large stone".

There are various types of megaliths. A single stone stand-

Photo. Géniaux

THE ALINEMENT NEAR CARNAC, BRITTANY

ing by itself is called a Menhir, "long stone", *men* being a Breton word for "stone". A big slab or boulder supported by other stones so as to form a chamber is called a Dolmen, "table stone", *dol* being the Breton word for "table" as "men" is for stone. Stones arranged in a circle are called Cromlechs, from the Gaelic word *crom*, "circle" or "curve", and *leac* (pronounced *lechk*), a "flag-stone". Some writers wrongly apply "cromlech" to structures which are really "dolmens". Two stones set up to support a stone lintel form what is known as a Trilithon. When a number of standing stones are arranged in open lines, the group is called an Alinement.

The oldest megaliths were set up as far back as the archæological Neolithic Age. The peoples of the Bronze Age and the Iron Age also erected them, however, and they were regarded with reverence in the British Isles well within the historic period. The early Christian teachers found it necessary to condemn what is known as "stone worship". In A.D. 452 the Council of Arles issued a decree against "infidels" who "worshipped trees, wells, or stones". The Council of Tours in A.D. 567 called upon the clergy to deal with those who did un-Christian things "at certain stones, or trees, or wells", and the Council of Toledo in A.D. 681 condemned those who "worshipped idols or venerated stones". Another Council at Toledo in A.D. 692 dealt with the same practices, while a Council at Rouen issued a decree against those who made vows at stones, &c., "as if any divinity resided there and could confer good or evil". In A.D. 789 the French Emperor Charlemagne issued a decree against the "foolish people" who worshipped "trees, stones, and wells".

King Canute, the eleventh-century King of England and

Denmark, forbade the heathenish adoration of the sun, moon, fire, wells, stones, and trees.

An old Irish-Gaelic poem states that in Ireland

> There was worshipping of stones
> Until the coming of Patrick.

A god of a stone circle was known in Ireland as "Crom Cruach", and the ancient poem says that St. Patrick destroyed this "feeble idol" with "a sledge-hammer". A prose manuscript states that Crom Cruach was "the King idol of Erin" and round him were "twelve idols made of stones". Human sacrifices were offered to Crom Cruach at Hallowe'en. The centre at which he was worshipped is near the village of Ballymagauran in County Cavan, and it was named "Magh Slecht", which means the "Plain of Adoration".

The old Gaelic poem referred to says of the idol of Crom Cruach:

> Brave Gaels used to worship it . . .
> He was their god. . . .
>
> To him without glory
> They would kill their piteous, wretched offspring
> With much wailing and peril,
> To pour their blood around Crom Cruach.
>
> Milk and corn
> They would ask from him speedily
> In return for one-third of their healthy children:
> Great was the horror and the scare of them.
>
> They did evil,
> They beat their palms, they pounded their bodies,
> Wailing to the demon who enslaved them,
> They shed falling showers of tears.

In St. Patrick's "Confession" it is told that Ireland was

given over to the worship of "idols and other abominations", and the Irish are warned that all those "who adore the sun shall perish eternally".

The standing stones on the "Plain of Adoration" were still in existence as late as the tenth century. In Ulster there was a stone idol called "Kermand Kelstach" which was kept in the porch of the cathedral of Clogher as late as the fifteenth century.

One of the Gaelic names for certain standing stones in Ireland and Scotland is "Stones of Worship". The custom was anciently common of erecting single stones (menhirs) as "boundary stones"; these marked the boundary of an estate or tribal area and were regarded as sacred. The Romans similarly adored a boundary stone which was supposed to be entered by the spirit of the god Terminus. This god's name still survives in the English word "terminus".

Menhirs were also erected by the ancient peoples of Ireland and Scotland to mark the sites of battles and the graves of famous men. A Gaelic story collected in Skye tells of a sorceress who struck a standing stone with a magic wand. The stone was immediately transformed into a warrior. Then she struck the warrior with the wand, and he immediately became a standing stone again. Evidently it was believed that the spirit of the dead warrior had entered the stone which had been erected to his memory.

Another Gaelic story tells that a goddess named Beira, who reigned during the winter, was pursued by a young god at the beginning of summer. To escape him she turned into a grey stone which always remained moist. It was anciently believed that there was "life" or a "spirit" in a stone from which moisture oozed.

Some standing stones are pierced with holes, and there are references to vows being taken by individuals who stood at either side of such a stone, and thrust their hands into the hole and clasped them. Hollows, called "cups", in some standing stones were struck by small stones, and then an individual pressed an ear against the hollow, believing that something prophetic could be heard.

In September, 1656, the Presbytery of Dingwall met in Applecross to deal with certain "heathenish practices" which were common in the western parts of the County of Ross. The minutes tell that "future events in reference especially to life and death, in taking of journeys, was expected to be manifested by a hole of a round stone wherein they tried the entering of their head".

If men found they could put their heads into the "hole" they "expected their returning to that place, and failing, they considered it ominous".

The minutes refer also to "the adoring of wells" and "superstitious monuments and stones". There is no reference to human sacrifice, but it is stated that bulls were sacrificed on 25th August, and that oblations of milk were poured upon the hills.

Standing stones appear to have been erected in ancient times for a variety of purposes. On the south side of Great Bernera Island in the Outer Hebrides, two menhirs overlook a narrow tidal channel, and may have been known as "landmarks" with a meaning understood by the ancient mariners. A standing stone 20½ feet high and 6½ feet broad, with a notch at one side near the top, is situated 80 feet above the sea-level and facing the Atlantic on the west coast of Lewis. It can be seen far out at sea, and it, too, may have been a landmark for the guidance of mariners. Seen from a distance it resembles a human hand. Its Gaelic name is "Stone of the Truiseal", but what "Truiseal" means is not known. An old Gaelic poem asks the "great Truiseal":

> "Who were the peoples in thine age?"

but the stone gives a very vague answer, saying it merely "longs to follow the rest" (the ancients), and that it is fixed "on my elbow here in the west".

Although we cannot tell what peoples before the Celts erected megaliths, and why all varieties of megaliths were erected and what purposes they served, it would appear that stones were regarded as sacred because it was believed spirits entered them and influences came from them.

The earliest known use that stones were put to was in the construction of graves. In ancient Egypt the dead were, as has been told, buried in the hot, dry sand. The bodies never decayed, but became naturally mummified. When graves were lined with stone, however, the flesh vanished and the bones alone remained. The curious belief then arose that the stone ate the flesh. The Greeks appear to have acquired this belief for they called a stone coffin a "sarcophagus", which means "flesh eater".

Dr. Elliot Smith has suggested that this belief about stone "eating" flesh may have given origin to the idea that the spirit as well as the flesh of a dead person entered the stone placed at or in a tomb. The ancient Egyptians put stone statues inside royal tombs and these were shut up in a special chamber. Apparently it was believed that the spirit would enter the statue.

It may be that some ancient seafaring peoples, who adopted

the Egyptian type of ship, also imitated the burial customs of Egypt. Professor T. Eric Peet has pointed out that the megalithic monuments "lie entirely along a natural sea route".

The Egyptians were the first people who quarried and made use of stone. They erected the great pyramids, and set up tall obelisks like "Cleopatra's Needle", which was taken from Egypt in modern times, and placed on the Thames Embankment, London. This "needle" is really a menhir, and to the Egyptians it was a symbol of sun worship.

The ancient seafarers who erected dolmens, menhirs, and stone circles in Britain, France, and elsewhere had not the skill of the Egyptians in dressing and polishing stone, but they were able to transport big boulders from place to place, and to set them up as monuments. The supported stones of some dolmens weigh from twenty to sixty tons. A great deal of skill and labour was required to raise them up and place them upon their stone supports. Big menhirs weighing many tons were dragged some distance and placed erect in holes prepared for them.

Large numbers of workmen were required to erect megaliths. The people who carried out the work must have lived, like the ancient Egyptians, in organized communities, and been accustomed to obey the commands of their rulers. They could not have been mere "savages running wild in the woods".

The most famous megalithic group in the British Isles is Stonehenge in Wiltshire. It originally consisted of an outer circle of about thirty upright blocks of sandstone, a second circle of smaller stones, an inner group of great trilithons in horse-shoe shape, and from 16 to 21½ feet high, and a further group of " blue stones " partly enclosing a big boulder called the " Altar Stone ".

The sandstone blocks had been dressed, and the tops of the upright stones in the outer circle and those of the horse-shoe group of trilithons were cut so that the lintel stones laid across them might be dovetailed and held securely.

Dolmen at Plas Newydd, Anglesey

The sandstone blocks were found by the prehistoric workers lying on Salisbury plain, but the " blue stones " are not native to the district and were transported from a distance.

Stonehenge was erected not later than fourteen hundred years before the Birth of Christ. The people who erected it appear to have been in touch with the colonies of seafarers in the Mediterranean area—colonies which were, in turn, in touch with ancient Egypt and Crete. The Egyptian blue-glazed beads, already referred to, have been found in graves of the early Bronze Age at Stonehenge and elsewhere in Wiltshire, and in Dorsetshire. These beads were of a type manufactured in Egypt between 1500 and 1250 B.C. No ancient European people could imitate "Egyptian blue".

The remains of great stone circles at Avebury in Wiltshire are very impressive. There the chief circle, which had about a hundred stones, was erected on a rampart of earth with a diameter of about 1200 feet. Inside this circle were two double circles. The stones were not, however, dressed as were those of Stonehenge.

Many other circles, and also dolmens and menhirs, are to be seen in England. Among the Scottish megaliths the most remarkable are the circles at Callernish in Lewis and Stennis in Orkney, which must have been erected by seafarers who for some reason established colonies in these outlying areas. About a mile from the Stennis stones is a remarkable ancient grave called Maeshow. It is a great mound of earth and stones about 300 feet in circumference and 36 feet high, surrounded by a trench about 40 feet wide. Inside the mound is a stone-built chamber about 15 feet square, the walls being about 13 feet high. Leading to this chamber is a low, narrow passage about 54 feet long.

A big ancient grave of similar type at New Grange, near Drogheda in Ireland, has also a long corridor leading to a stone-built chamber. Ireland has other interesting tombs and a number of stone circles.

In Brittany there are a good many passage tombs with chambers. The best known is on the island of Gavr' inis, Morbihan. Its mound is about 200 feet in diameter, and the chamber, which is about 6 feet high, is circular, and is roofed by a great block of stone measuring 13 feet by 10. The passage is 40 feet long. Other "passage tombs" are found in Spain and on the island of Sardinia, in southern Italy, at Tunis in north Africa, and in Palestine. These tombs appear to be relics of seafaring peoples from the Ægean area.

Brittany is very rich in megaliths. The most famous group is the alinement near Carnac in Morbihan. Its stones spread east and west for a distance of about 3300 yards and number about 1169. At Erdeven there are 1129 stones in ten lines. There are also many imposing dolmens.

Megaliths are found in Sweden, Denmark, and north Germany, but they are not very common in Holland and Belgium. They are numerous, however, in Britain and Ireland, France and Spain, in Sardinia, Corsica, and Malta. There are a few in the south-east corner of Italy and none in Greece, but some in Bulgaria. Megaliths are found along the north coast of Africa, from Morocco to Tripoli, and in West Africa. There are some examples in the Soudan. In Asia they are found in Palestine and Syria, in Persia, in India, in the Dutch East Indies, and in Japan and Korea.

It is possible that the megaliths are relics of some ancient religious cult which was spread far and wide by seafaring peoples who came under its influence at various periods. The megaliths are not everywhere of the same age. Some were erected when Neolithic implements were in use, and others when bronze and iron implements supplanted those of stone. Religious beliefs were not, however, changed when new implements were introduced. As we have seen, stone worship had not died out in Scotland and Ireland until early Christian times.

CHAPTER XXIII

Ancient Races and Languages

In former times it was customary to divide the races of mankind into four main colour groups. These were the Red men, the Yellow men, the White men, and the Black men.

Although we still use these ancient colour terms, other physical characters are now taken into account, such as head shape, stature, the type of hair, &c.

The first main classification, however, is that which divides mankind into ancient and modern groups. Among the ancient men the most distinctive were the Neanderthals. As has been shown, they used Mousterian tools. Their heads and bodies had outstanding peculiarities which are not found in any existing race. They had very pronounced eye-brow ridges, no chins, very short necks, peculiar ribs, peculiar thumbs, bent knees, and short shin-bones. This Neanderthal race became extinct at the close of the Fourth Glacial epoch.

The earlier Piltdown race is represented by a single skull—or rather, by fragments of a skull. Except that the skull was not of Neanderthal type, we cannot say much about the race it represents. This race was, however, nearer to the Modern Man species than was the Neanderthal; at the same time it had primitive characters.

The earliest known representatives of Modern Man are the Grimaldis and the Cro-Magnons. Two skeletons of the Grimaldi races were discovered in an "Infants' Cave" near Mentone—the one is the skeleton of a woman and the other of a lad. As the jaws of this type protrude, some have called the Grimaldis "negroid". Dr. Elliot Smith, as we have seen, compares the Grimaldis, however, to the dark natives of Australia who have been largely displaced by the modern Australians of European type.

The Cro-Magnons had heads, faces, and bodies very like those of modern Europeans. We do not know whether they had dark or fair hair, or if their eyes were brown, grey, or blue, or whether there were dark and fair Cro-Magnons.

The Cro-Magnon skulls were long, but their cheek bones were so broad and high that their faces seemed broader than those of other long-headed types. As a rule, long-headed types have long faces and broad-headed types broad faces. The illustrations on the following page show the shapes of typical long and broad heads.

There were two types of Cro-Magnons—the tall Cro-Magnons and the short Cro-Magnons.

The Cro-Magnon head is still found in modern Europe. In the Dordogne valley, France, those who have Cro-Magnon heads are mainly dark-haired and brown-eyed and of short or medium stature. The same type is met with among the Berbers of north Africa. Groups of modern Cro-Magnons have also been detected in Brittany, and on the islands of northern Holland. Some scientists are of opinion that there is a Cro-Magnon blend in Scotland, where high cheek-bones are fairly common, and in parts of western England and Ireland. The fair northern type has rather flat cheek-bones.

The Cro-Magnons practised the Aurignacian industry, which was followed in turn by the Solutrean and Magdalenian industries.

During the Solutrean epoch a long-headed race of different type from the Cro-Magnons appeared in central Europe.

It is known as the Brünn race. Skulls found in Austria and Hungary show that the Brünn foreheads sloped backward

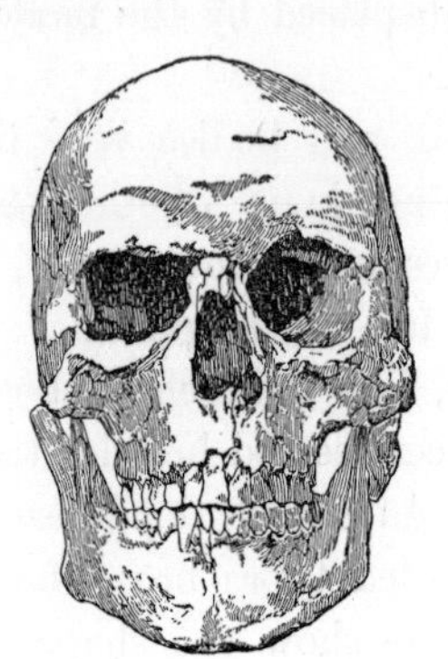

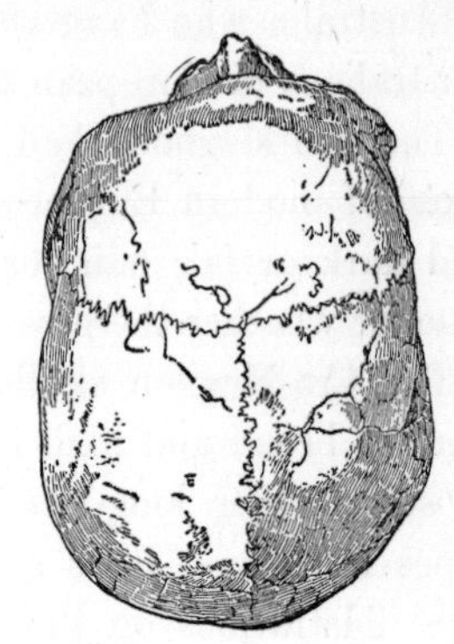

Long-head (Dolichocephalic) Skull

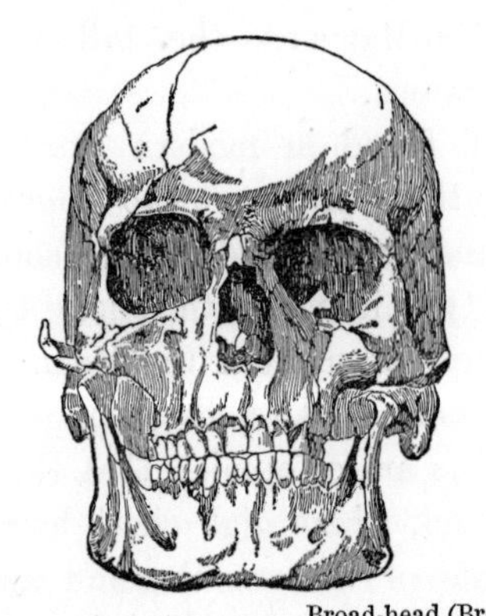

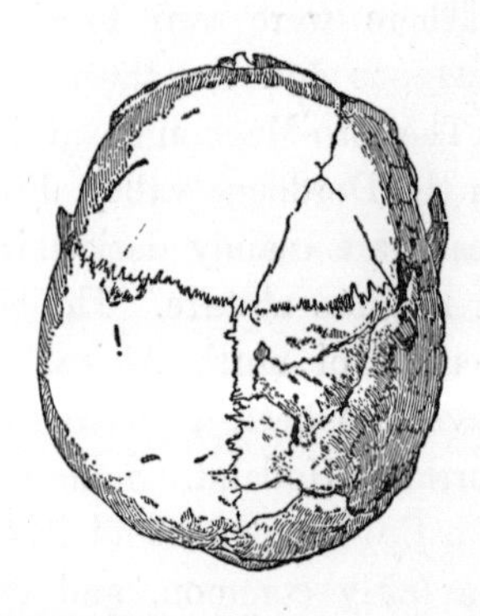

Broad-head (Brachycephalic) Skull

Both these specimens were found in "Round" Barrows in the East Riding of Yorkshire.

and were not so well developed as those of the Cro-Magnons, the cheek-bones were neither broad nor high and the faces were narrow. The limb bones of this type indicate high stature. It appears, too, from the character of the bones, that the Brünn people had powerful necks and shoulders.

In Magdalenian times (that is, during the final phase of Palæolithic civilization) the Cro-Magnons were the chief race in western Europe. Traces of other types have been found, however. A skeleton which has been named "Chancelade" was discovered at the rock shelter of Raymonden in France, and it has been compared to the modern Eskimo type. A third type shows Cro-Magnon skulls of broadened character, suggesting a blend of the long-headed Cro-Magnon race with a broad-headed race which probably came from Asia during the latter part of the Palæolithic Age.

At the close of the Magdalenian period groups of peoples practising the Azilian and Tardenoisian industries entered Europe. In the cave of Ofnet in Bavaria over thirty skulls of Azilio-Tardenoisian Age have been discovered. Some are of broad-headed type and some of long-headed type. In western Europe the long-headed type was commonest during this period, but a few broad-headed skulls have been found.

In northern Europe during the same period the Maglemosian industry was practised by a people of whom no skulls have been found. This industry passed into Britain across the North Sea land-bridge and is represented in northern England and in western Scotland. In the Oban area, as has been shown, there are traces of Maglemosian influence. The domesticated dog was possessed by the Maglemosians of the Baltic area, but not by the Azilians of Spain and France. Bones of the domesticated dog were found in the MacArthur Cave, Oban, and also human skulls which are of "intermediate type"—partly of Iberian type and partly of Nordic (Scandinavian) type. It is possible, therefore, that the "carriers" of the Maglemosian industry were fair northerners, and the carriers of the Azilian industry dark, short men of the type which was most common in Britain and in western Europe when the Neolithic industry was introduced.

Dr. Elliot Smith states with "the utmost confidence" that the Neolithic peoples of the British Isles, western France, the Iberian peninsula (Spain and Portugal), the Mediterranean littoral, and north-east Africa were "linked together by the closest bonds of affinity". They were of the same type as the pre-dynastic Egyptians. The men were about five feet five inches in stature, and the women about five feet; they had black or dark brown hair, which was sometimes curly, and dark eyes and long skulls. Their bodies were of slender build, the bones being "singularly slight and free from pronounced roughness and projecting bosses that indicate great muscular development". In the pre-dynastic Egyptian graves Dr. Elliot Smith noted an interesting peculiarity of this race. The "atrophy and fusion of the bones of the small toe, often ascribed to the wearing of boots in modern times", was as common among the "bootless" people of sixty centuries ago as it is nowadays.

This short, dark type is known as the "Mediterranean race", and the western European branch of it is usually referred to as "Iberian".

As the Iberians who practised the Neolithic industry introduced agriculture into ancient Britain, they became more numerous than the earlier hunting peoples of the dark and fair types.

"When," says Dr. Collignon, the French ethnologist, "a race is well seated in a region, fixed to the soil by agriculture, acclimatized by natural selection, and sufficiently dense, it opposes, for the most precise observations confirm it, an enormous resistance to absorption by the newcomers, whoever they may be."

In Britain the short, dark Iberian peoples occupied the western areas chiefly. It is possible that the oldest megalithic monuments were erected by them. The western rural areas of England and Scotland are still, on the whole, occupied by darker types than the eastern areas.

After bronze came into use, broad-headed peoples entered Britain in increasing numbers. Their graves are of the "short-barrow" type, while those of the Iberian peoples of the Neolithic Age are of the "long-barrow" type. They appear to have settled in largest numbers along the east coast.

When iron came into use a people who burned their dead invaded Britain, but as their skulls were destroyed on the funeral pyres, we cannot say anything definite about their racial connexions.

The chief races of Europe were, after the introduction of metals, three in number. In northern Europe the commonest type was the tall, fair northern or Nordic race; in western and southern Europe the Mediterranean (Iberian) race was in the majority. The third race was broad-headed, and appears to have come from Asia. Owing to its prevalence in the Alpine area, it has been called the "Alpine race"; another name, which is now becoming more common, is the "Armenoid race" because the type is so common in Armenia. The bones of the broad-headed type have large bosses, indicating strong muscular development. The Armenoids are the heavy and muscular people, but it was the slight, nimble-brained Mediterranean race that laid the basis of modern civilization by discovering and introducing agriculture, inventing boats, working stone, and making use of metals.

In addition to these three races there were groups of the descendants of the Cro-Magnon and other races in various areas. These groups are sometimes referred to as "pockets".

During the European period, when iron was used for weapons and bronze for shields and helmets, the Celtic peoples swept into western Europe. They came from the Danube area, and Greek writers describe them as tall and fair. "Their children have generally white hair," says one Greek writer, "but as they grow up their hair assumes the colour of their fathers' (yellow or light brown)." The same writer (Poseidonius) tells that

> "The Iberians (of Western Europe) and the Celts had in bygone times waged a war of long duration for the land; but at length they entered into an alliance and held the country in common. Marriage alliances effected a fusion of the two peoples. It was because of the intermixing that they are said to have received the name of Celtiberians."

The Celts mixed with other peoples, including the Greeks. As there were Celtiberians in western Europe, there were Gallo-Grecians in northern Greece. Numerous Celts entered northern Italy, where fair types are still to be found.

As they were tall and fair, the Celts appear to have been a branch of the northern or Nordic race, which is also called the Teutonic race. In historic times, however, the Celts and Teutons waged wars for centuries for political supremacy not only on the Continent but in Britain.

In ancient Egypt broad-headed peoples of Armenoid type began to settle, although not in great numbers, towards the close of the prehistoric or pre-dynastic period. They became more numerous later, especially during the period when the pyramids were being erected. The masses of the people were, however, of the Mediterranean racial type, and the fellaheen of modern Egypt are mostly representatives of ancient proto-Egyptians of the pre-dynastic age.

The early Cretans were mainly of the long-headed, dark type—that is, of the same race as the pre-dynastic Egyptians. There was, however, a minority of "broad heads". In modern Crete the long-headed types are still the commonest. Intermediate types are more numerous than pure "broad-headed" types.

The dark, long-headed type was well represented in Lower Mesopotamia in Sumerian times. The Semitic type appears to have been a blend of the dark, long-headed race of Arabia, and the Armenoid race of Asia Minor.

In Persia and India the intermediate type—mixed long and broad heads—was common in ancient times. There were also in India dark races, which are now referred to as Dravidians and pre-Dravidians. The latter were not related to either the Armenoid or the Mediterranean races. Nor were the negroid peoples of Africa.

A very distinctive people in Asia is known to us as the Mongolians. They have yellow skins, broad heads, very small noses, and inward sloping eyes. During the Ice Age and the post-Glacial period the ancestors of modern Mongolians were separated from the other races in Asia for thousands of years.

The "Red Indians" of Northern America have sometimes been referred to as "Mongolians". Typical Red Indians, however, have large and curved noses and straight eyes. Their type in Asia is, according to Dr. Elliot Smith, still represented in the Trans-Caspian area and especially "near the head-waters of the Yenisei". Some Red Indian peoples on the western coast of the North American continent have, however, Mongolian characters—inward sloping eyes and small noses. In South America the racial types differ considerably in some areas from the Red Indian "beak-nosed" type of North America. Some resemble the south-eastern Asiatics and the Polynesian type has also been detected.

The Polynesian type is found in the Pacific islands known as Oceania. It is mainly of intermediate type—that is, a mixture of broad-heads and long-heads. The seafarers of Polynesian type originally reached the coral islands from Indonesia. It is represented to-day in parts of Java and Sumatra, and even along the shores of India and Ceylon. Dr. Elliot Smith is of opinion that the Polynesians are descendants of the ancient seafarers from the Persian Gulf and Syria who founded colonies along the sea-coasts of southern and south-eastern Asia in ancient times.

A darker Oceanic people with negroid features is known as the Melanesians. They are the descendants of peoples who in ancient times had adopted the seafaring mode of life from the pioneers who sailed the earliest ships in Far Eastern waters.

It is not possible nowadays to find, in every area, evidence of the race movements of the ancient peoples. Later migrations and conquests have destroyed all traces of the pioneers who introduced into some districts the elements of civilization. Withal, many areas have yet to be explored by archæologists.

The fair northern race appears to have sent out groups of world-wide wanderers in ancient times. A fair people with blue eyes, known to the Chinese as the Wu-suns or Usuns, occupied part of Chinese Turkestan and fought against the

Chinese as far back as 200 B.C. The Sacæ (Scythians) of central Asia appear also to have been mainly fair.

Some antiquaries state that the Biblical Amorites of Syria and Palestine were, in the main, fair or red-headed people. Fair peoples filtered into north Africa during the early dynastic age of Egypt and are depicted in some of the tomb pictures with light hair and blue eyes. Fair types are to be found in the Berber communities in north Africa, and they are represented among the Atlas Mountains in Morocco. A tall, fair people called the Gaunches were formerly in the Canary Islands. Some are of opinion that the Gaunches were descended from the Cro-Magnons. They lived in caves and decorated them and used weapons of wood and obsidian. Of special interest is the fact that they mummified their dead. In the *Proceedings of the Royal Society of Medicine* (Vol. XX, part vi), Mr. Warren R. Dawson has shown that their methods of mummification were remarkably like those of the ancient Egyptians of the twenty-first dynasty (1090–945 B.C.). We know that during this period wood was being carried from Morocco to Egypt, for Mr. A. Lucas, chemist, Department of Antiquities, Egypt, has found that the sawdust from mummy packings (dated about 1000 B.C.) was derived from the Atlas cedar and not from the cedar of Lebanon (*The Cairo Scientific Journal*, Vol. III, No. 32). The ancient seafarers appear to have ventured beyond Morocco and reached and influenced the isles of the Gaunches.

In view of such evidence we should ever be careful not to confuse the questions of race and culture. Discoveries and customs were passed on from one race to another, and when the "carriers" happened to be mariners, the elements of a distinctive culture might be suddenly transplanted to an alien country far separated from the area of origin. The imported customs were then mixed with local customs.

Interesting as the race problem may be, it must be borne in mind that it is not, and never has been, so important a consideration as that of nationality. Peoples unite in areas to form nations, not because their heads are long or broad, or because their hair is dark or fair, or their eyes brown, blue, or grey, but because they have interests in common and ideals in common. Nor should a race be confused with a language, because one particular language may be spoken by peoples of different racial types in a single nation or in a single empire. The English language is spoken in our day in our own land by broad-heads and long-heads, by fair-haired, brown-haired, and black-haired peoples, by tall peoples and short peoples, by the descendants of the ancient Teutons, Celts, and Iberians.

There is no general rule with regard to changes of language. In some areas the language of the conquerors has been adopted; in other areas the language of the conquerors has died out as the language of the Normans has died out in England. A minority may impose its language on a majority, or it may not. The languages of trading peoples are inclined to spread to distant areas, and to be adopted by various peoples speaking different languages. In our own day the English language is spoken by Chinese, Red Indians, and Africans. In America the descendants of African slaves and many descendants of Red Indians have lost their original languages and speak English only. Similar changes may have taken place in ancient times, and a language may have entirely died out in the original home area and be spoken only in some distant colony or by the descendants of ancient wanderers from the homeland who settled in distant parts. There are a great many distinctive languages among the Red Indians and other pre-European peoples in North and South America which cannot nowadays be traced in Asia.

The languages of the great ancient civilizations have died out. The ancient Egyptian, Sumerian, and Cretan languages are, for instance, no longer spoken. The Latin language of the Romans has ceased to be used as an everyday speech. Its influence, however, survives in modern Italian, Spanish, French, &c., and to a lesser degree in English. A language is an artificial thing—an invention of man, and it undergoes many changes in the process of time. If an ancient Angle or Saxon were to come to life to-day, he would be unable to understand the English language which we now speak and write.

In the past great civilizations have grown, flourished, and decayed like their languages. The ancient "cradles of civilization" in Egypt, Mesopotamia, and Crete influenced wide areas, but all cradles are found, in time, to be too small, and these areas lost their importance when vigorous and well organized peoples in other areas made new discoveries and new inventions, and, advancing farther on the path of progress, extended their influence to more and more distant parts of the world.

The study of ancient man, to which this book is devoted, is one which extends our interest in humanity, and broadens our outlook upon life. It prepares us for the study of economic history, for it enables us to regard existing social institutions in their relation to the fundamental conditions upon which they are based. Withal, this study arouses interest in the science of geology, for we are prompted by the story of early man's experiences to visualize the various changes which occurred in the world before the earth's surface assumed its present form; and it also introduces us to the sciences of anatomy and archæology. Of much importance, too, is the training which this interesting study affords in dealing with fragmentary evidence—in piecing together such facts as come to light so as to construct a connected narrative. It therefore helps to develop the faculty of constructive imagination—a faculty which aids one in every walk of life in dealing with the future as well as the past. All great soldiers and sailors, statesmen and business men have been men with constructive imaginations—men with what is known as "vision".

The study of ancient man is withal a fascinating "hobby" for our leisure hours, which can be pursued in any part of the world, and no matter in what walk of life we may be engaged. Fresh evidence is constantly coming to light, and much remains to be discovered so that our knowledge may be extended and our natural interest in life further enlarged.

INDEX